Houghton Mifflin Reading

Practice Book

Level 1.1–1.2

HOUGHTON MIFFLIN

Practice Book

Illustration:
Priscilla Burris 2, 106-107, 111, 113, 119, 123, 128, 131, 135, 141-142, 153, 155-158, 165, 172-173, 190; Abby Carter 30-33; Rusty Fletcher 53, 59, 62, 69, 71, 76, 86-87, 90, 95-96, 101-102, 117-118, 130, 132, 136, 144, 145-146; Lisa Chauncy Guida 1-7, 12; James G. Hale 151-152, 159, 164, 167, 183, 185-187; Megan E. Jeffery 36-41; Loretta Lustig 9, 11-13; John Magine 18-24; Tate Nation 42-45, 47-48, 58, 63, 79, 80, 85, 97-99; Diane Palmisciano 148, 150, 161, 170, 176, 178-179, 181; Cary Pillo 25-27, 29, 54, 56, 60-61, 66, 77, 81-83, 88, 103-104, 108-109, 120-121, 127, 133-134, 137; Karen Lee Schmidt 15-17, 35, 49-51, 105, 114-115, 124-126, 129, 139, 143, 147, 149, 162-163, 171, 174, 177, 179, 182, 184; Bari Weissman B-16, 35, 55, 57, 73, 89, 160, 166, 169; Liza Woodruff 64-65, 67, 72, 74-75, 78, 92-93. Notebooks and paper by Nathan Jarvis.

Photography:
Photographs by Ralph J. Brunke Photography.

ISBN: 978-0-5471-9541-4
17 18 19 0928 18 17 16 15
4500534107

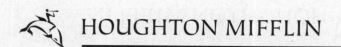

HOUGHTON MIFFLIN

Contents

Contents

Punchouts

Name _____

What Happened?

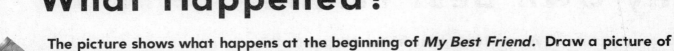

The picture shows what happens at the beginning of *My Best Friend.* Draw a picture of something that happens in the middle of the story. Then draw what happens at the end.

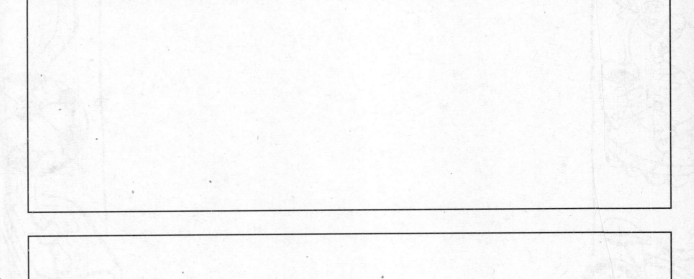

Name _____

My Own Best Friend

 Draw a picture of you and your best friend doing something you love to do together.

Alphabet Review

Andy Apple

Benny Bear

Callie Cat

 **Penmanship Practice**

A A a a

B B b b

C C c c

Name _____

Begins with Bb or Cc

Phonics Circle each picture whose name begins like the Alphafriend's name.

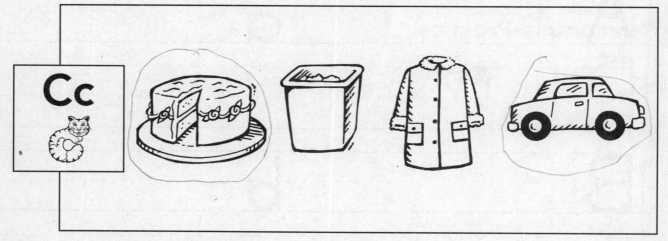

Word Play Name the picture. Print the letter that begins the picture name.

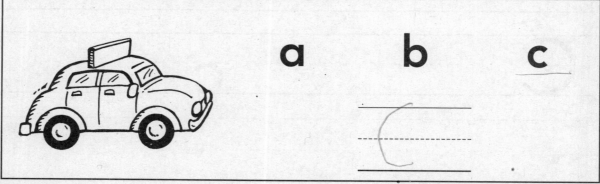

Name _____

Alphabet Review

Dudley Duck

Edna Elephant

✏️ Penmanship Practice

D D D D D D   d d d d d d d d

E E E E E E   e e e e e e e

Name _____

The Letters Dd and Ee

Phonics Draw a line from the Dd to pictures whose names begin with that letter sound.

Draw a line from the E to the matching letters.

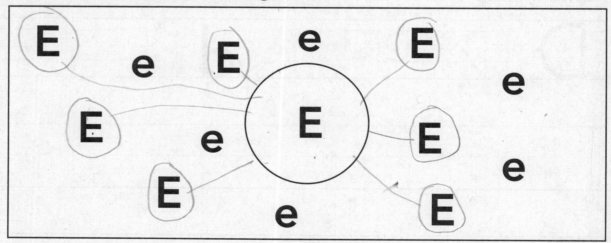

Word Play Name the picture. Print the letter that begins the picture name.

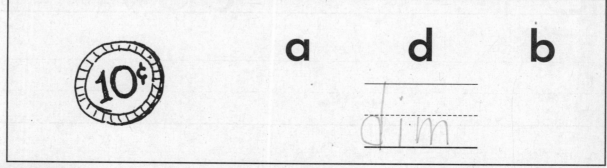

Name _____

Alphabet Review

Fifi Fish

Gertie Goose

Hattie Horse

✏ Penmanship Practice

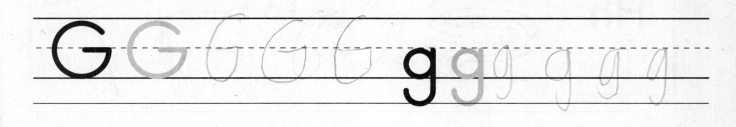

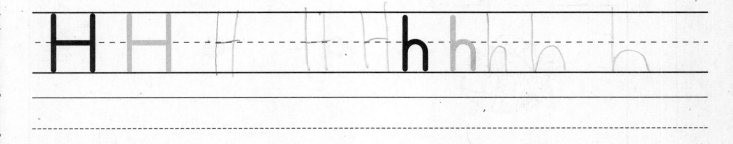

Name _____

Begins with Ff, Gg, or Hh

Phonics Circle each picture whose name begins like the Alphafriend's name.

Word Play Name the picture. Print the letter that begins the picture name.

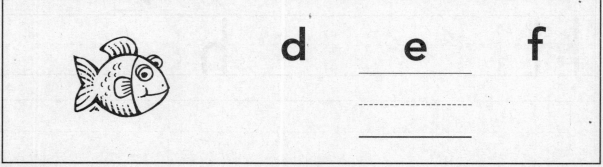

d   e   f

Name _____

Alphabet Review

Iggy Iguana

Jumping Jill

✏️ Penmanship Practice

Name _____

The Letters Ii and Jj

Phonics Draw a line from the i to the matching letters.

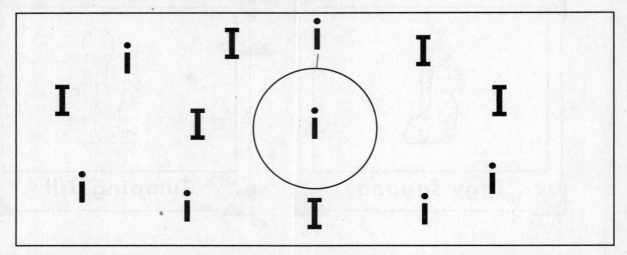

Draw a line from the Jj to the pictures whose names begin with that letter sound.

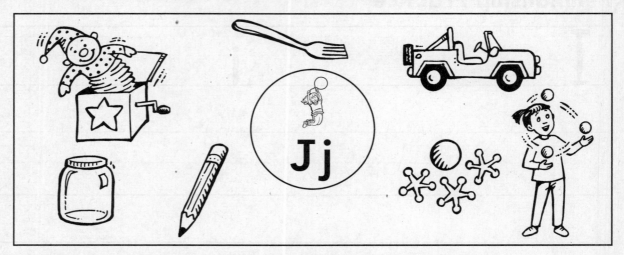

Word Play Name the picture. Print the letter that begins the picture name.

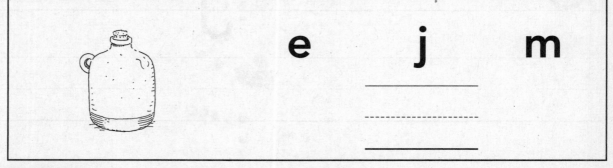

e   j   m

Name _____

Alphabet Review

Keely Kangaroo

Larry Lion

Mimi Mouse

Penmanship Practice

K K   k k

L L   l l

M M   m m

Name _____

Begins with Kk, Ll, or Mm

Phonics Circle each picture whose name begins like the Alphafriend's name.

Word Play Name the picture. Print the letter that begins the picture name.

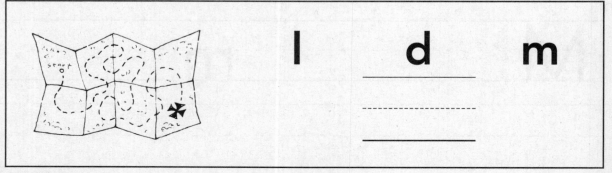

l   d   m

_____
- - - - - - - - - - - - -
_____

Name _____

Alphabet Review

Nyle Noodle

Ozzie Octopus

Pippa Pig

Penmanship Practice

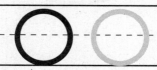

Name _____

Begins with Nn or Pp

Phonics Circle each picture whose name begins like the Alphafriend's name.

Word Play Name the picture. Print the letter that begins the picture name.

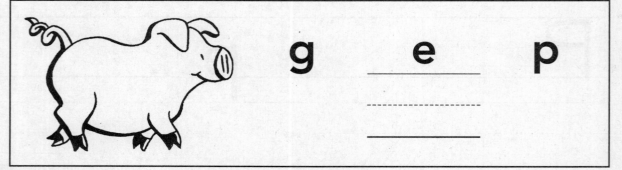

g ___ e ___ p

Name _____

Alphabet Review

Queenie Queen

Reggie Rooster

Sammy Seal

 Penmanship Practice

Q Q   q q

R R   r r

S S   s s

Begins with Qq, Rr, or Ss

Phonics Circle each picture whose name begins like the Alphafriend's name.

Word Play Name the picture. Print the letter that begins the picture name.

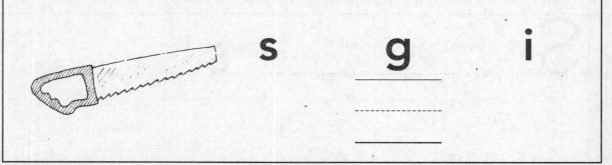

s   g   i

Name _____

Alphabet Review

Tiggy Tiger

Umbie Umbrella

Vinny Volcano

Penmanship Practice

Name _____

Begins with Tt or Vv

Phonics Circle each picture whose name begins like the Alphafriend's name.

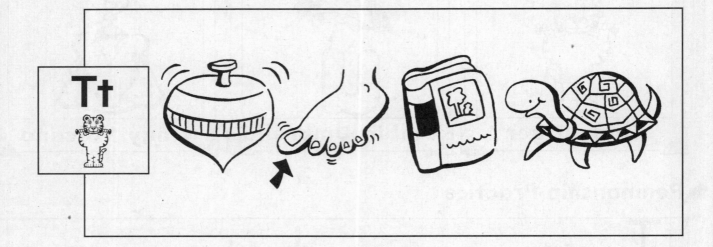

Word Play Name the picture. Print the letter that begins the picture name.

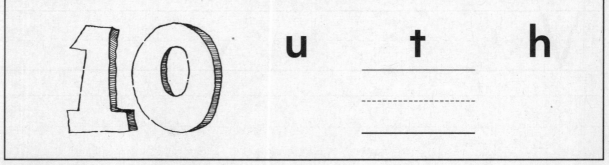

u   t   h

Name _____

Alphabet Review

Willy Worm

Mr. X-Ray

Penmanship Practice

W W   w w

X X   x x

Name _____

The Sounds for Ww and Xx

Phonics Draw a line from the Ww to the pictures whose names
begin with that letter sound.

Draw a line from the Xx to the pictures whose names
have the /ks/ sound.

Word Play Name the picture. Print the letter that begins the picture name.

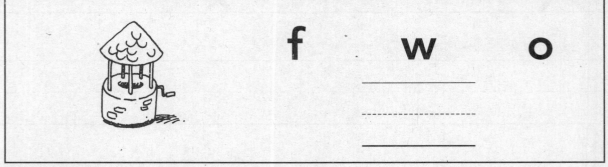

f   w   o

Name _____

Alphabet Review

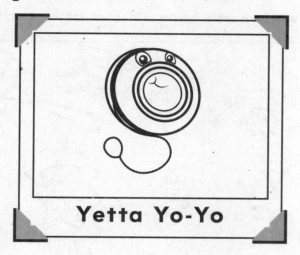

Yetta Yo-Yo

Zelda Zebra

✏️ Penmanship Practice

Y Y   y y

Z Z   z z

Name _____

Begins with Yy or Zz

Phonics Draw a line from the Yy to pictures whose names begin with that letter sound.

Phonics Draw a line from the Zz to pictures whose names begin with that letter sound.

Word Play Name the picture. Print the letter that begins the picture name.

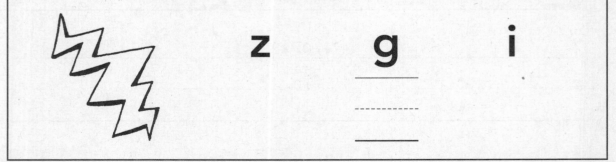

z   g   i

Begins with *m, s, t, c*

Think of each beginning sound. Write m, s, t, or c.

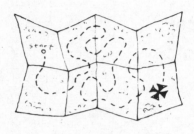

1. _____

2. _____

3. _____

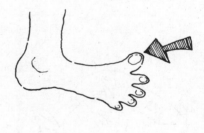

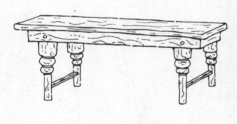

4. _____

5. _____

6. _____

7. _____

8. _____

9. _____

Theme 1: **All Together Now**   **1**

Name _____

Ends with *m*

Name each picture. Color the pictures whose names have the same ending sound as  .

 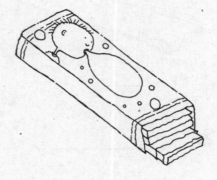

 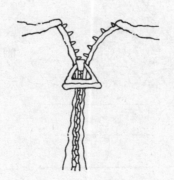 

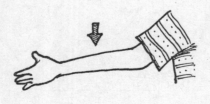  

Name _____

Ends with *s*

Name each picture. Color the pictures whose names have the same ending sound as  .

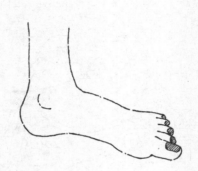

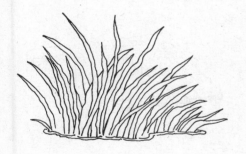

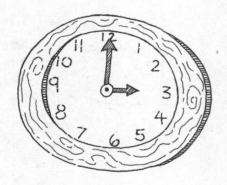

Name _____

Ends with *t*

Name each picture. Color the pictures whose names have the same ending sound as 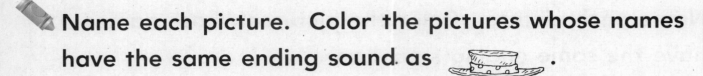 .

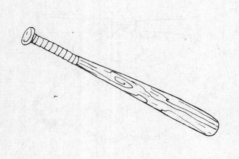

Name _____

Short *a*

Name each picture. Color the pictures whose names have the same vowel sound as  .

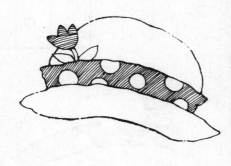

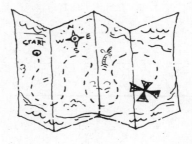

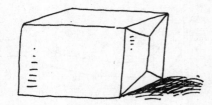

Blending Short *a* Words

Blend the letter sounds. Then write the correct word for each picture.

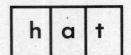

1.

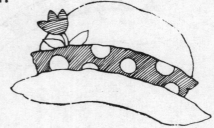

_____

- - - - - - - - - - - - - - -

_____

2.

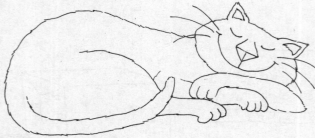

_____

- - - - - - - - - - - - - - -

_____

Read the sentence. Circle the picture that goes with it.

3. **Sam sat.**

Name _____

Begins with *m* or *s*

Think of each beginning sound.

Write **m** or **s**.

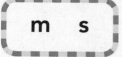

1. _____

2. _____

3. _____

4. _____

5. _____

6. _____

Name _____

Put Them in Order!

✂ **Cut out and paste the pictures in the correct order.**

1.

2.

3.

Theme 1: **All Together Now**   9

Name _____

Words to Know

Write a word from the box to complete each sentence.

Word Bank

go	the	on

_____

1. Go, cat, _____ !

_____

2. The cat sat _____ the mat.

_____

3. The mat sat on _____ cat.

Theme 1: **All Together Now**   **11**

Name _____

Begins with *t* or *c*

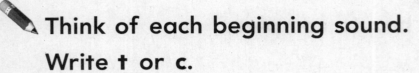

Think of each beginning sound.

Write **t** or **c**.

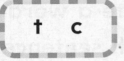

t   c

1. _____

2. _____

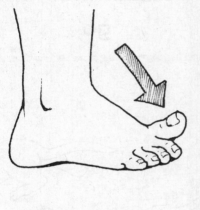

3. _____

4. _____

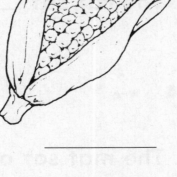

5. _____

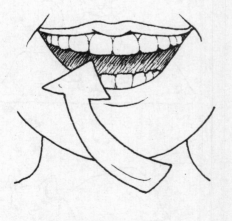

6. _____

12   Theme 1: **All Together Now**

Name _____

Where Did the Cat Sit?

Cut out the two pictures that show where the cat sat in the story. Paste them in the spaces to show the correct order.

The cat sat.   **The cat sat.**

| 1 | 2 |

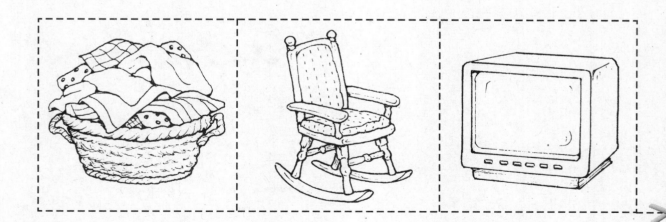

Theme 1: **All Together Now**   13

Name _____

Who Did It?

Circle the answer to each question.

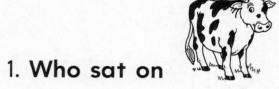

1. Who sat on ?

_____

2. Who can go?

Name _____

The Mat

 Circle the sentence that tells about each picture.

1.

Go, Cat!

Cam Cat sat on the mat.

2.

Go, Cam Cat!

Cam Cat sat.

3.

The mat sat on Cam Cat.

Go!

Name _____

Giving Details

Draw a picture of two friends playing together. Write labels that tell who and what.

Name _____

Begins with *n*, *f*, or *p*

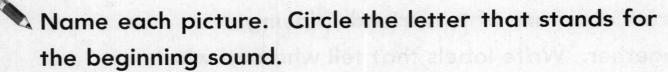

Name each picture. Circle the letter that stands for the beginning sound.

1. n f p	2. n f p	3. n f p	4. n f p
5. n f p	6. n f p	7. n f p	8. n f p
9. n f p	10. n f p	11. n f p	12. n f p
13. n f p	14. n f p	15. n f p	16. n f p

Name _____

Ends with *n*

Name each picture. Color the pictures whose names have the same ending sound as  .

Name _____

Ends with *f*

 Name each picture. Color the pictures whose names have the same ending sound as 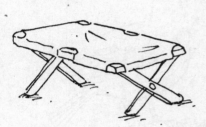.

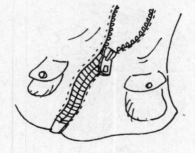

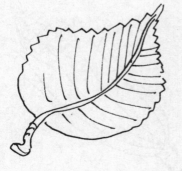

20 Theme 1: **All Together Now**

Name _____

Ends with *p*

Name each picture. Color the pictures whose names have the same ending sound as 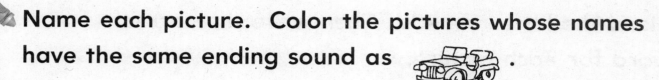 .

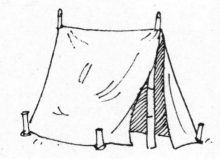

Name _____

Blending Short *a* Words

Blend the letter sounds. Then write the correct word for each picture.

| m | a | p | | c | a | p | | c | a | t | | m | a | n |

1. _____

2. _____

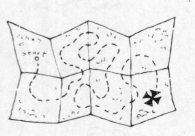

3. _____

4. _____

Words with Short *a*

Read the words in each box. Draw a line from the correct word to the picture.

cat		fat	
cap		fan	
pan		mat	
pat		man	
cat		Pam	
cap		pan	
cat		pat	
can		pan	

Name _____

Begins with *n* or *f*

Think of each beginning sound.
Write **n** or **f**.

n f

1. _____

2. _____

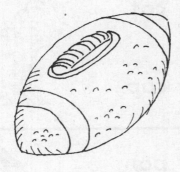

3. _____

4. _____

5. _____

6. _____

Name _____

What's Different?

Look at both pictures. Which things in the
pictures are different? Put an X on them.

Name _____

Words to Know

Write a word from the box to complete each sentence.

Word Bank

and	jump	not

_____
- - - - - - - - - - - - - - - - -
1. Nan can _____ !

_____
- - - - - - - - - - - - - - - - -
2. Nan _____ Pat can jump here, too.

_____
- - - - - - - - - - - - - - - - -
3. We can _____ jump here.

Name _____

Words to Know

✂ Cut out and paste each sentence next to the picture it matches.

1. [   ]

2. [   ]

3. [   ]

Can we jump, too?

We can not go here.

We can jump and jump.

Name _____

Begins with _p_

Name each picture. Color the pictures whose names have the same beginning sound as

  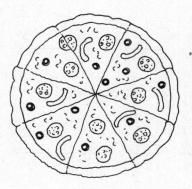

  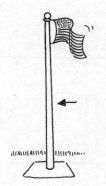

Theme 1: **All Together Now**   **29**

Name _____

Nan and Fan Can!

  Write Nan or Fan to tell what the characters in Nan and Fan can or can not do.

_____
- - - - - - - - - - - - - - - - - -

1. _____ can jump.

2. _____ can not jump.

3. _____ can not pat the cat.

4. _____ can pat the cat.

5. _____ can go.

6. _____ can not go.

Nan

Fan

Name _____

Story Words

Write a word from the box to complete each sentence.

Word Bank

draw	read	write

1. Pat can _____ .

2. Pam can _____ .

3. Pat and Pam can _____ .

Name _____

Look What We Can Do!

 Read each sentence. Draw a line from the picture to the sentence that tells about it.

1.

Pam can read.

Pat can read, too.

2.

Pam can write.

Nat can write, too.

3.

Pam and Pat can go.

Pam, Nat, and Pat can fan.

Name _____

Giving Details

Draw a picture of your favorite thing to do at school. Write labels that tell where and what.

Name _____

Begins with *b*, *g*, *h*, *r*

Name each picture. Circle the letter that stands for the beginning sound.

1. b r g	2. h r g	3. b g h	4. r g h
5. b r g	6. b r g	7. h r g	8. b r g
9. b g h	10. r g h	11. b g h	12. b r h
13. b r h	14. b r g	15. b r h	16. r g h

Theme 1: **All Together Now**   35

Name _____

Ends with *b*

 Name each picture. Color the pictures whose names have the same ending sound as  **.**

Name _____

Ends with *g*

Name each picture. Color the pictures whose names have the same ending sound as 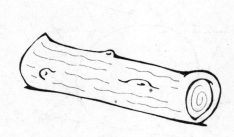.

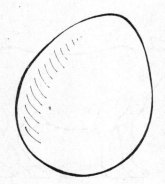

Name _____

Ends with *r*

Name each picture. Color the pictures whose names have the same ending sound as ☆.

Name _____

Short *i*

✏️ Name each picture. Color the pictures whose names have the same vowel sound as  .

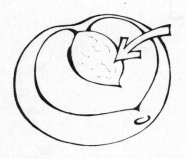

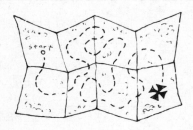

Name _____

Blending Short *i* Words

Blend the letter sounds. Then write the correct word for each picture.

| p | i | g | | h | i | t | | b | i | b |

1.

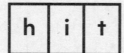

_____
- - - - - - - - - - - - - -
_____

2.

_____
- - - - - - - - - - - - - -
_____

3.

_____
- - - - - - - - - - - - - -
_____

Name _____

Short *a* and *i*

Read the words in each box. Draw a line from the correct word to the picture.

pit pig		fit fig	
big bag		pat pig	
had hit		sit bit	
fit fig		hit ham	

Name _____

Begins with *b* or *h*

Think of each beginning sound.

Write **b** or **h**.

1. _____

2. _____

3. _____

4. _____

5. _____

6. _____

Name _____

What Happened?

Look at each picture. Draw a line from the picture of what happened to the picture showing why it happened.

What happened?	**Why?**

1.

2.

3.

Words to Know

Write a word from the box to complete each sentence.

Word Bank

find	have	who

_____
- - - - - - - - - - - - - - - - - -
1. Can Pat _____ Nan?

_____
- - - - - - - - - - - - - - - - - -
2. We _____ one pig and a cat.

_____
- - - - - - - - - - - - - - - - - -
3. _____ can go to the mat?

Name _____

Words to Know

✂ Cut out and paste each sentence next to the picture it matches.

1. _____

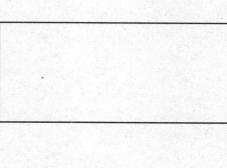

2. _____

3. _____

Who can find the bat?

Who can jump to the hat?

We have one cat and a pig.

Theme 1: **All Together Now**   45

Name _____

Begins with *r* or *g*

Think of each beginning sound.

Write **r** or **g**.

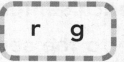

r   g

1. _____   2. _____   3. _____

4. _____   5. _____   6. _____

Theme 1: **All Together Now**   **47**

Name _____

Who Can Hit?

Read each sentence. Draw a line from the picture to the sentence that tells about it.

1.

   We have a big bat.

   Sam can hit.

2.

   Go, Sam, go!

   Pat can hit, too.

3.

   Nat hit one big hit.

   We ran, ran, ran!

48 Theme 1: **All Together Now**

Name _____

At the Farm

Write a word from the box to complete
each sentence.

Word Bank

| carrot | farm | feed |

1. Nan can go to the

_____

- - - - - - - - - - - - - - - - - - -

_____ !

2. Big Pig can have a

_____

- - - - - - - - - - - - - - - - - - -

_____ .

_____

- - - - - - - - - - - - - - - - - - -

3. The man can _____
Big Pig.

Theme 1: **All Together Now**   49

Name _____

Big Pig's Farm

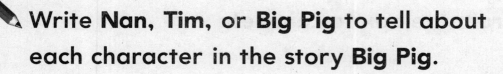 Write **Nan**, **Tim**, or **Big Pig** to tell about each character in the story **Big Pig**.

Big Pig

1. The big hat can fit

   _____

   _____ .

   _____

   ----

2. _____ can feed

   Big Pig a fig.

   _____

   ----

3. _____ can feed

   Big Pig a carrot.

   _____

   ----

4. _____ can go!

Tim

Nan

Name _____

Using Exact Words

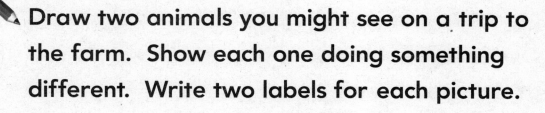 Draw two animals you might see on a trip to the farm. Show each one doing something different. Write two labels for each picture.

Write a sentence about each animal and what it is doing.

_____

- -

_____

- -

_____

Name _____

Begins with *d*, *w*, *l*, or *x*

Name each picture. Circle the letter that stands for the beginning sound.

1. d w l	2. d l x	3. w x d	4. x l d
5. l x w	6. w l d	7. d w l	8. l d w
9. w d l	10. d l w	11. d x w	12. l d w
13. d x l	14. l d w	15. w x d	16. w d l

Name _____

Ends with _d_

✏️ **Name each picture. Write d if the word ends like Ted. Then draw a line from Ted to his bed.**

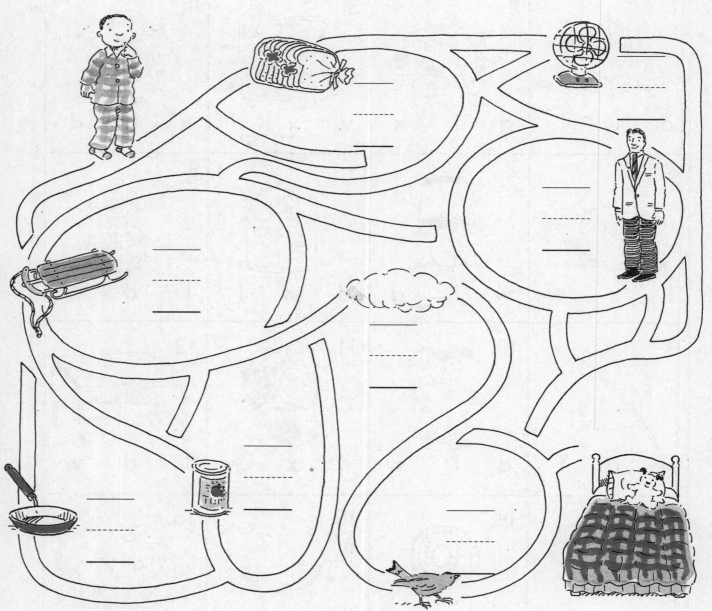

Name _____

Ends with /

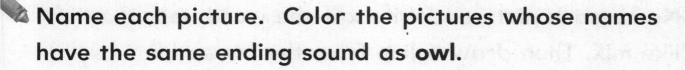

Name each picture. Color the pictures whose names have the same ending sound as **owl**.

Theme 2: **Surprise!**   55

Name _____

Ends with *x*

✏ Name each picture. Write **x** if the word ends like **mix**. Then draw a line from the fox to his box.

Name _____

Blending Short *o* Words

Blend the letter sounds. Then write the correct word for each picture.

| h | o | t | | b | o | x | | m | o | p | | d | o | t |

_____

- - - - - - - - - - - - - - - - -

_____

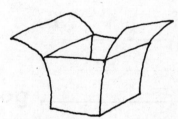

_____

- - - - - - - - - - - - - - - - -

_____

_____

- - - - - - - - - - - - - - - - -

_____

_____

- - - - - - - - - - - - - - - - -

_____

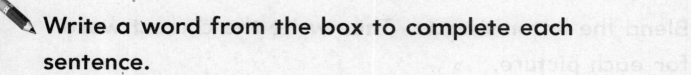
Name _____

Words with Short *o*

✎ Write a word from the box to complete each sentence.

Word Bank

| on | fox | box |

_____

1. Go, _____, go!

_____

2. The fox sat _____ the ox.

_____

3. The ox sat on the _____ !

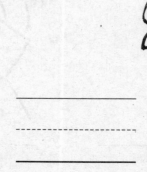

Name _____

Short *a*, *i*, and *o*

✏️ **Write a word from the box to name each picture.**

Word Bank

map	pig	pot	dog	pat	mop

1.

   _____

2.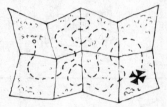

   _____

3.

   _____

4.

   _____

5.

   _____

6.

   _____

Name _____

Begins with *d* or *l*

✏️ **Name each picture. Think of the beginning sound. Write d or l.**

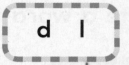

1.

2.

3.

4.

5.

6.

7.

8.

9.

10.

11.

12.

Name _____

Who Can Find It?

Read each sentence.   Follow the directions.

Color a cat with one bat.

Color an ox in a big hat.

Name _____

Words to Know

Draw a line from each story to each picture that shows what the story is about.

1. **What have we here?**

    We have one, two, three.

    We have four and five!

2. **A cat can sit.**

    It can sit upon a box.

    It can sit in the box, too.

3. **Can the cat fit in?**

    It fit in the box once.

    The cat got too big!

Name _____

Words to Know

Circle the sentence that tells about each picture.

1. One cat sat upon a box.

   We jump here.

2. Five sit.

   Three have hats.

3. A man can bat.

   Once, the four wigs fit in here.

4. What can we find?

   We have a big pan.

Words with *w* or *x*

✏ **Name each picture. Circle the pictures whose names begin with w. Write w if the word begins with w.**

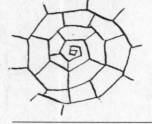

1. _____   2. _____   3. _____

4. _____   5. _____   6. _____

✏ **Write x to complete each word. Draw a picture for each word.**

fo____

bo____

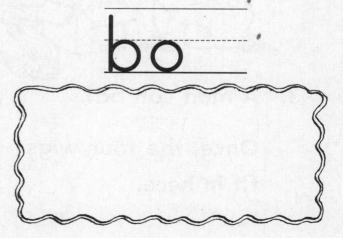

Name _____

What's in the Box?

 Read each sentence. Draw a line from each picture to the sentence that tells about it.

1.   A fox can fit in the box.

2.   A pig can fit, too.

3.   A hat can fit in the box.

4.   Dot got the box.

5.   Dan and Dot can fit, too.

6.   Dot can find a lot in the box.

Wigs, Wigs, Wigs!

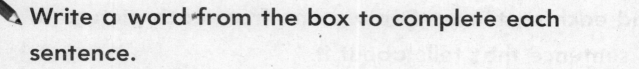

Write a word from the box to complete each sentence.

Word Bank

| ball | thanks | shelf | win | wigs |

1. What can Nat Cat _____ ?

2. What is on the _____ ?

3. Can Nat Cat win _____ ?

4. Get a _____ , Nat Cat.

5. _____ , Dot Dog!

Name _____

About the Story

Circle the picture that answers each question.

1. Who can hit the ball in?

2. What can Pat Pig win?

3. What can Pat Pig find in the box?

 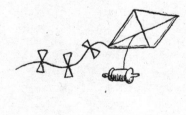 

4. Who got the thanks?

Name _____

Using Exact Words

 Draw two different things people can do at a
fair. Write two labels for each picture.

 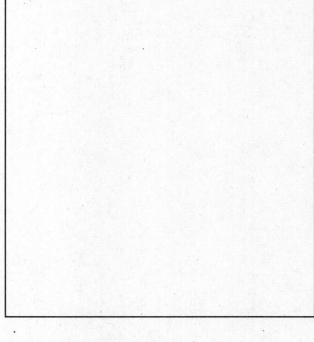

Write two sentences. Tell what is happening in
each picture.

_____

- -

_____

_____

- -

_____

Name _Christian_

Begins with *y*, *k*, or *v*

Name each picture. Circle the letter that stands for the beginning sound.

1. ⓨ v k	2. k v ⓨ	3. y ⓥ k	4. v y ⓚ
5. k ⓥ y	6. ⓚ y v	7. k ⓥ y	8. ⓨ v k
9. v y ⓚ	10. k ⓥ y	11. k ⓨ v	12. y ⓚ v
13. k y ⓥ	14. k v ⓨ	15. ⓚ y v	16. ⓨ k v

Name _Christian_

Ends with *k*

✎ **Name each picture. Write k if the word ends like look. Write g if the word ends like big.**

> k   g

72 Theme 2: **Surprise!**

Name ___Christian___

Blending Short e Words

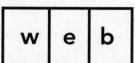 Blend the letter sounds. Then write the correct word for each picture.

w	e	b

b	e	d

n	e	t

t	e	n

1. ___ten___

2. ___web___

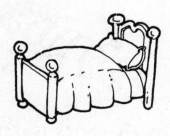

3. ___bed___

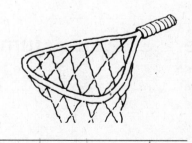

4. ___net___

Theme 2: **Surprise!**   **73**

Name _____

Words with Short *e*

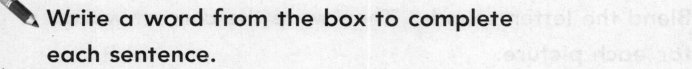

Write a word from the box to complete each sentence.

Word Bank

ten	bed	pet	get

1. I am in ___bed___ .

2. We can ___get___ a box.

3. The ___pet___ jumps in.

4. We have ___ten___ cats.

Name _____

Short *a*, *e*, *i*, and *o*

Read the words in each box. Draw a line from the correct word to the picture.

pat		met	
pot		men	
wag		pan	
wig		pen	
ten		hit	
tan		hen	
dig		vet	
dog		vat	

Name _____

Begins with *y* or *v*

Name each picture. Think of the
beginning sound. Write **y** or **v**.

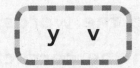

1.	2.	3.
4.	5.	6.
7.	8.	9.
10.	11.	12.

Name _____

Could It Really Happen?

Look at each picture. If the picture shows something that could really happen, color it.

Name _____

Words to Know

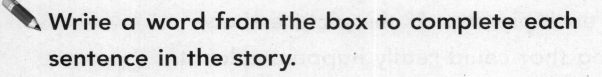

Write a word from the box to complete each sentence in the story.

Word Bank

I	my	for	do

_____

1. "I have _____ bat," said Van.

_____

2. Dot said, "I _____ not have a bat."

_____

3. Van said, "The bat is _____ me. The bat is for you, too."

_____

4. Dot said, " ___ can hit. You can hit, too."

78 Theme 2: **Surprise!**

Name _____

Words to Know

Write a word from the box to complete each sentence in the story.

Word Bank

me	is	said	you

_____

1. "What can I do for you?" _____ the vet.

_____

2. "My pet _____ here," I said.

_____

3. "Can you get my pet for _____ ?" I said.

_____

4. "Here _____ go," said the vet.

Name _____

Begins with *k*

 Name each picture. Color the pictures that
have the same beginning sound as **kit**.

Name _____

Vets Can Help

Read each question. Circle the correct answer.

1. **Who is Big Ben?**

   Big Ben is a pet cat.

   Big Ben is a pig.

2. **Who can do a lot for Big Ben?**

   Ken can do a lot.

   The vet can do a lot.

3. **Who is in the pen?**

   A big pet is in the pen.

   A cat is in the pen.

4. **Who is in the van?**

   Nan is in the van.

   The vet is in the van.

5. **What can the vet do?**

   The vet can do a lot for the big pet.

   The vet can get the hen in the pen.

Name _____

Wanted: Soup!

Write a word from the box to complete each sentence in the story.

Word Bank

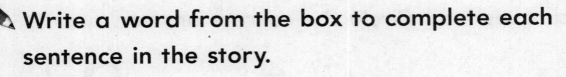

soup   fire   wanted   vat   noodle

1. Dan lit the _____ .

2. Dan wanted hot _____ soup.

3. Dan got a _____ .

4. Pat _____ noodle soup, too!

5. Pat and Dan can have hot _____ .

Name _____

Put Them in Order!

✂ Cut out and paste the sentences in the order that they happened in the story.

1.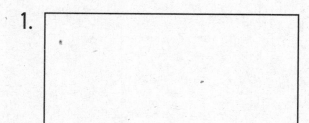

2.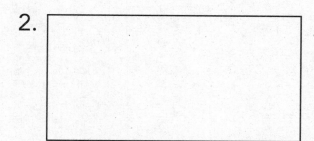

3.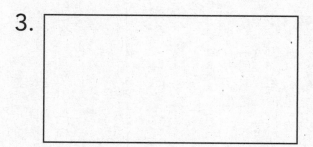

4.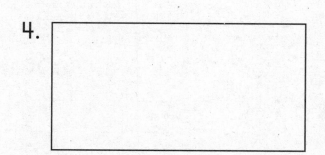

Fox got hot noodle soup.

Fox lit a hot fire.

Ox wanted hot fox soup.

Fox wanted hot hen soup.

Name _____

Using Words That Are Just Right

Cross out the word that is the same in each sentence. Write a better word from the box.

Word Bank

brown	large	long	new
red	small	square	tall

1. The librarian works in a ~~big~~ room. _____

_____

2. She has a ~~big~~ desk. _____

_____

3. Here is a ~~big~~ pile of books. _____

_____

4. A ~~big~~ sign reads "Quiet." _____

Begins with *qu*, *j*, or *z*

Name each picture. Circle the letter that stands for the beginning sound.

1.	2.	3.	4.
j qu z	z qu j	qu j z	j z qu

5.	6.	7.	8.
j z qu	j qu z	j z qu	qu j z

9.	10.	11.	12.
j qu z	z qu j	z j qu	z qu j

13.	14.	15.	16.
z j qu	z j qu	qu j z	z qu j

86 Theme 2: **Surprise!**

Name _____

Short *u*

Name each picture. Color the pictures whose names have the same vowel sound as .

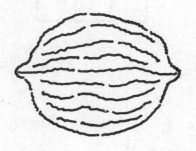
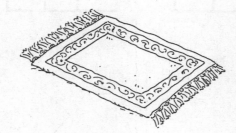

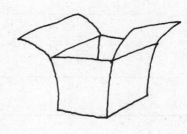

Name _____

Blending Short *u* Words

Blend the letter sounds. Then write the correct word for each picture.

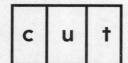 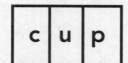 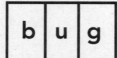 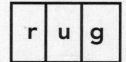

1.

_____

- - - - - - - - - - - - - - - - - -

_____

2.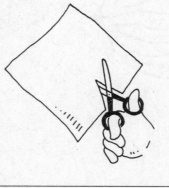

_____

- - - - - - - - - - - - - - - - - -

_____

3.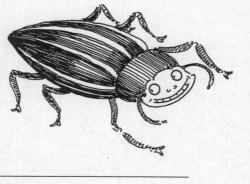

_____

- - - - - - - - - - - - - - - - - -

_____

4.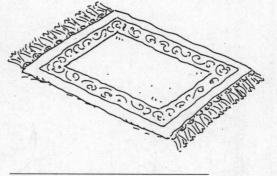

_____

- - - - - - - - - - - - - - - - - -

_____

Name _____

Short *a, e, i, o,* and *u*

Read the words in each box. Draw a line from the correct word to the picture.

jet jug		rug rig	
bug bag		mat mug	
nut not		hit hut	
hug hog		cut cat	

Name _____

Begins with *j* or *z*

Name each picture. Think of the
beginning sound. Write **j** or **z**.

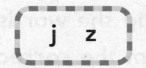

1.	2.	3.
4.	5.	6.
7.	8.	9.
10.	11.	12.

Name _____

Think of the Story

Think about Chapter 2 from the story **What Can a Vet Do?** Answer the questions.

1. Who is in the story?
   _____
   -
   _____

2. Where do they live?
   _____
   -
   _____
   _____
   -

3. What is the problem? _____
   _____
   -
   _____
   _____
   -

4. How is the problem solved? _____
   _____
   -
   _____

Name _____

Words to Know

✏️ **Write a word from the box to complete each sentence in the story.**

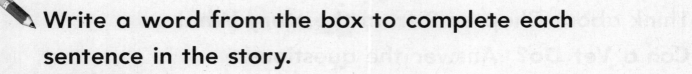

Word Bank

| does | away | pull | live | are | they |

1. The pet can get _____ .

2. Where _____ the pet go?

3. He can _____ the mat.

4. Can _____ find the pet?

5. They _____ wet.

6. The pet can _____ here!

Name _____

Words to Know

Cut out and paste each sentence under the picture it matches.

1.

2.

3.

Where are Pat and Dan?
Pat and Dan go away.

Where do Dot and Jan live?
They pull in here.

Does Ken live here?
He does!

Name _____

Begins with *qu*

 Name each picture. Color the pictures whose names begin like quit. Write qu.

1.	2.	3.
4.	5.	6.
7.	8.	9.

Name _____

Think About Zig Bug

✏ **Circle the answer for each question.**

1. What is a cot for Zig Bug?

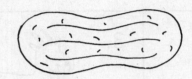   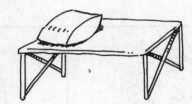

2. What is a jug for Zig Bug?

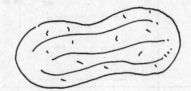   

3. What is a rug for Zig Bug?

4. What is a cup for Zig Bug?

5. What is a hut for Zig Bug?

A pot is a hut.   **A box is a hut.**

Name _____

Tug Away!

Read the words in the box. Write the correct word to finish each sentence in the play.

Word Bank

| rope | I'm | outside |

Narrator: We are _____ .

Get set for the big tug.

Elephant: I have a _____ .

I am big, and I can tug Hippo.

Hippo: _____ big, too.

I can tug a lot.

I can get Elephant to quit!

Who Is It?

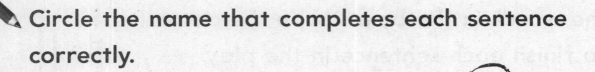

Circle the name that completes each sentence correctly.

1. ____ can not get in the hut.

    Rat   Elephant   Hippo

2. ____ can get a big rope.

    Hippo   Elephant   Rat

3. Hippo and ____ tug, tug, tug.

    Elephant   Rat   Hippo

4. But they can not pull ____ .

    Hippo   Rat   Elephant

5. Elephant and ____ quit.

    Hippo   Elephant   Rat

6. ____ does a jig.

    Elephant   Hippo   Rat

Name _____

Using Words That Are Just Right

Cross out the word that is the same in each sentence. Write a better word from the box.

Word Bank

busy	large	kind	new
round	square	sweet	tall

1. Our town has a good market. _____

2. Mom and I get good apples there. _____

3. We got a good cake for Dad. _____

4. The man that helps us is good. _____

Double Final Consonants

**Read each sentence. Circle the word that
ends with a double consonant and write it
below.**

1. It is fall.

2. Do we have a bass yet?

3. We can add to
   the can.

4. We have to fill the can!

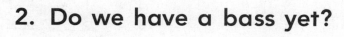

1. _____

2. _____

3. _____

4. _____

Name _____

Ending Sounds

Write a word from the box to complete each sentence in the story.

Word Bank

| sat | pack | is | has | bag |

_____

Jack has to _____ .

_____

Can Mack fit in the _____ ?

_____

Jack _____ to go.

_____

Mack _____ in the back.

_____

Jack sat. Mack _____ .

They can go!

Name _____

Words with Short *a*

Name each picture. Write *a* if the picture
name has the short *a* sound.

1.	2.	3.	4.
5.	6.	7.	8.
9.	10.	11.	12.
13.	14.	15.	16.

Name _____

Words with Short *a*

 Read each sentence. Circle the picture of the underlined word. Write the word.

1. **What is in the <u>bag</u>?**

   _____

   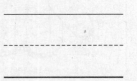  

2. **We have a <u>yam</u>.**

   _____

   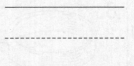  

3. **We have a <u>ham</u>.**

   _____

   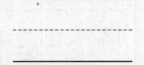  

4. **We have <u>jam</u>, too.**

   _____

    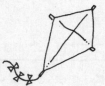

5. **Do you have a <u>tack</u>?**

   _____

Name _____

More Than One

Read each sentence. Circle the picture of the underlined word.

1. Where are the <u>animals</u>?

2. Ben has <u>cats</u>.

3. Nan has <u>hens</u>.

4. Kit has a <u>pig</u>.

What's It All About?

Read **Big Cats.** Then look at the chart. The
topic and main idea are filled in. You add the
details.

Big Cats

What can big cats do?

Big cats can jump.

Big cats can sit, too.

Big cats can live in dens.

Big cats are not pets!

Topic	Big cats
Main Idea	A big cat can do a lot.
Details	

Name _____

Words to Know

Write a word from the box to complete each sentence in the story.

Word Bank

| animal | full | see | flower |

It Is Cold

"Look!" said Zack.

_____

"I _____ a bird."

"Look!" said Jack.

_____

"I see an _____ .

_____

It is _____ of nuts."

"Look!" said Pat.

_____

"I have a fall _____ here."

Name _____

Words to Know

✏ Look at the picture. Then read each question and circle the answer.

1. **Where is the animal?**

2. **Where is the bird?**

   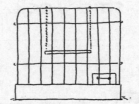

3. **What is full of nuts?**

4. **Who has the flower?**

Where We Live . . .

Write a word from the box to complete each sentence in the story.

Word Bank

| leaves | snow | summer | winter |

We live in the South.

It can get cool in the fall.

_____

We jump in the _____ .

It does not get too cold in the _____ .

We do not get _____ .

Spring is not too wet.

_____

We dig in the _____ .

We can add coal to a "snowman"!

Name _____

What Season Is It?

Cut out and paste the sentences under the picture they tell about.

1. **Spring**

2. **Summer**

3. **Fall**

4. **Winter**

It can get wet. We can find a flower.	It can get cold. Snow can fall.
It can get cool. Leaves can fall.	It can get hot. We fan to get cool.

Name _____

The Short *a* Sound

Write a word from the box to complete each sentence in the story.

an

at

can

cat

had

man

_____

1. My pet is _____ animal.

_____

2. It is a _____ .

_____

3. A _____ let me have the cat.

_____

4. He _____ a lot of cats.

_____

5. My cat _____ do a lot.

_____

6. Look _____ my cat jump!

Name _____

Make a Sentence

 Draw a line from the part of the sentence
that names a person or object to the part
of the sentence that tells what the person or
object can do.

1.  **We**   can live in a den.

2.  **A fox**   can live in huts.

 Write the sentences you made.

_____

1. _____

_____

_____

2. _____

_____

_____

114   Theme 3: **Let's Look Around!**

Spelling Spree

Use the letter shapes to write three
Spelling Words.

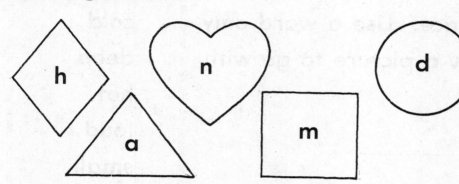

an
at
can
cat
had
man

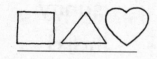

1. _____ 2. _____ 3. _____

Proofread each sentence. Circle each Spelling Word
that is wrong, and write it correctly.

_____

4. I see a big kat. _____

5. Look ad it go! _____

6. It ken jump, too. _____

Name _____

Using Sense Words

Write a sense word from the box to finish each sentence. Use a word only once. Then draw a picture to go with your sentences.

_____

1. It was a _____ winter day.

2. The wind sounded _____.

3. The snow on the grass looked _____.

4. The ice felt _____.

Name _____

Verb Endings -s, -ed, -ing

Read each sentence. Circle the sentence that tells about each picture.

1. Nan is looking for Jill to play.

   Ken looks for a bug.

2. Nan kicked the can.

   Nan sees Jill.

3. Nan is going to dig.

   Nan is going to jump.

4. Nan and Jill jumped.

   Nan and Pat filled the box.

Name _____

Words with Short *i*

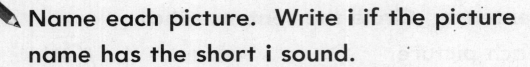

Name each picture. Write i if the picture name has the short i sound.

1.	2.	3.	4.
5.	6.	7.	8.
9.	10.	11.	12.
13.	14.	15.	16.

Name _____

Words with Short *i*

Read each sentence, and circle the picture of the underlined word. Write the word.

1. Ben is <u>six</u>.

_____
- - - - - - - - - - -
_____

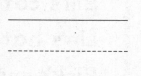  

2. He is looking for a <u>mitt</u>.

_____
- - - - - - - - - - -
_____

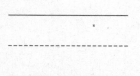   

3. The <u>wig</u> is not for Ben.

_____
- - - - - - - - - - -
_____

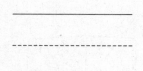   

4. The <u>bib</u> fits Em.

_____
- - - - - - - - - - -
_____

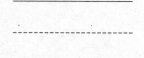  

5. The cap is for <u>him</u>.

_____
- - - - - - - - - - -
_____

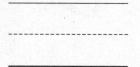  

Name _____

Whose Is It?

Write the words from the box under the picture they name.

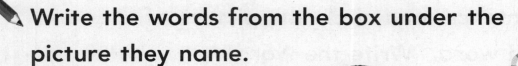

| Jill's box |
| Bill's cat |
| Lin's hat |
| Rick's mitt |

1.

_____

- - - - - - - - - - - - - - - - - - - -

_____

2.

_____

- - - - - - - - - - - - - - - - - - - -

_____

3.

_____

- - - - - - - - - - - - - - - - - - - -

_____

4.

_____

- - - - - - - - - - - - - - - - - - - -

_____

Name _____

What Happens Next?

✂ **Cut out and paste a picture to show what happens next.**

1.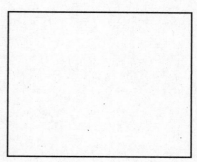

2.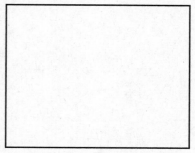

✂

Name _____

Words to Know

Draw a line from the sentences to the picture they tell about.

1. Bill got the paper first.

2. "Look at the paper, Dad!"
   said Bill.
   The paper said, "Come eat
   at Kit's!
   All kids can have a dip and
   a bit to eat."

3. "Shall I call Kit's?" said Bill.
   "I have never had a dip at
   Kit's."

4. "Why not?" said Dad.
   "Every kid will go. Get set."

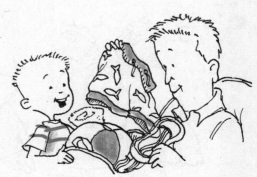

Theme 3: **Let's Look Around!**   **123**

Name _____

Words to Know

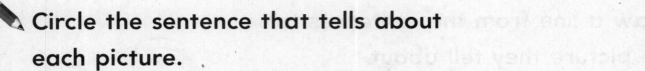 Circle the sentence that tells about each picture.

1.

"Why do we jump?" said Dot Hen.

"Look at the paper first," said Dot Hen.

2.

"Call all the hens to eat," it said.

"I never see all the animals," said Fox.

3.

"Every flower looks tan," said Fox.

"Shall I call Pig to eat, too?" said Dot Hen.

Name _____

Dinner Time

Write a word from the box to complete each sentence in the story.

Coyote set up a big sign.

_____

"Eat _____ at my den," it said.

Word Bank

trick

dinner

dish

sign

_____

Hen and Pig looked at the _____ .

"We can go," said Pig.

A sign at the den said, "Sit in the _____ ."

_____

"It is a _____ !" said Pig.

"What a bad coyote," said Hen.

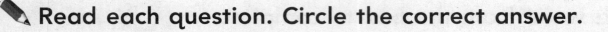

Name _____

What's for Dinner?

✏ **Read each question. Circle the correct answer.**

1. **Who got a paper for a dinner?**

   Hen, Fox, Pig, and Coyote got a paper.

   Pig, Hen, and Fox got a paper.

2. **Where is the dinner?**

   The dinner is at Mr. C's den.

   The dinner is at Pig's hut.

3. **Who is Mr. C?**

   Mr. C is a big cat.

   Mr. C is a coyote.

4. **What did Coyote do to get the animals to sit?**

   He said, "It is not a big, bad trick."

   He said, "I will eat one of you."

5. **What did the animals have for dinner?**

   They had figs and nuts.

   They had yams.

Name _____

The Short *i* Sound

Write a word from the box to complete
each sentence in the story.

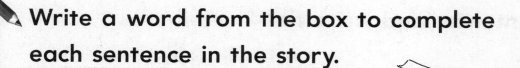

Spelling Words

in

it

him

big

sit

did

_____
- - - - - - - - - - -

1. Dad _____ not
   see me.

_____
- - - - - - - - - - -

2. I filled a box for _____ .

_____
- - - - - - - - - - -

3. The _____ box looked full.

_____
- - - - - - - - - - -

4. I said to Dad, "You can _____ here."

_____
- - - - - - - - - - -

5. Dad said, "What is _____ the box?"

_____
- - - - - - - - - - -

6. I said, "Look in _____ and see!"

Theme 3: **Let's Look Around!**   127

Name _____

Naming Parts

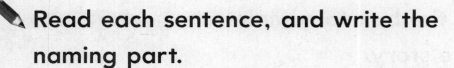 Read each sentence, and write the naming part.

1. Tim runs. _____

2. The cat sits. _____

3. The pot falls. _____

4. Dad gets the flowers. _____

128 Theme 3: **Let's Look Around!**

Name _____

Spelling Spree

Write the missing letter to complete each Spelling Word. Then write the word.

in

it

him

big

sit

did

1. d___d   _____

2. h___m   _____

3. ___t   _____

Proofread each sentence. Circle each Spelling Word that is wrong, and write it correctly.

4. The pig is bige.   _____

5. The pig is en a pen!   _____

6. The pig can zit.   _____

Order Words

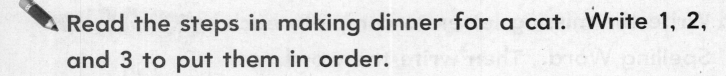 Read the steps in making dinner for a cat. Write 1, 2, and 3 to put them in order.

feed the cat	get the food	fill the dish

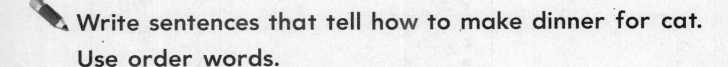 Write sentences that tell how to make dinner for cat. Use order words.

Order Word	Action	Thing

Order Word	Action	Thing

Order Word	Action	Thing

Name _____

Clusters with *r*

Name each picture. Circle the letters that stand for the beginning sounds.

1. cr pr fr	2. fr br tr	3. br gr tr	4. pr gr tr
5. br cr tr	6. br dr fr	7. br gr tr	8. cr dr tr
9. cr fr pr	10. cr pr fr	11. br dr pr	12. br fr pr
13. br fr pr	14. cr pr fr	15. dr fr pr	16. tr fr dr

Theme 3: **Let's Look Around!**   131

Name _____

Clusters with *r*

Circle the word that names each picture.
Write the word.

1.

brick   **brim**

_____

- - - - - - - - - - - - - - - - - - -

_____

2.

grab   **grass**

_____

- - - - - - - - - - - - - - - - - - -

_____

3.

drag   **drip**

_____

- - - - - - - - - - - - - - - - - - -

_____

4.

crib   **crab**

_____

- - - - - - - - - - - - - - - - - - -

_____

5.

trap   **trip**

_____

- - - - - - - - - - - - - - - - - - -

_____

6.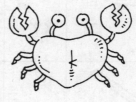

crack   **crab**

_____

- - - - - - - - - - - - - - - - - - -

_____

Name _____

Contractions with 's

Rewrite each sentence. Use a word from the
box in place of the underlined words.

Word Bank

| He's | It's | What's | Where's | Who's |

1. <u>Who is</u> calling you?

   _____

   _____

2. <u>He is</u> my dad.

   _____

   _____

3. <u>Where is</u> my hat?

   _____

   _____

4. <u>What is</u> in the box?

   _____

   _____

5. <u>It is</u> Dad's hat!

   _____

   _____

Which Is Which?

 Use the words in the box to list words under
Can Eat or **Can Not Eat.**

Word Bank

ham	crab	brick	jam
fox	map	ribs	hill

Can Eat	**Can Not Eat**
_____	_____
_____	_____
_____	_____
_____	_____
_____	_____
_____	_____

Name _____

Words to Know

Read the story. Color the picture that matches the story.

"Look!" said Kris. "I see many animals!"

"Me, too!" said Brad.

Kris said, "I see some green and brown frogs!"

"Me, too!" said Brad.

Kris said, "And I also see a bird as blue as my cap!"

"Me, too," said Brad.

"I like to look at the colors of all the pets," said Kris.

"Me, too!" said the bird.

"Funny bird!" said Brad.

Name _____

Words to Know

Read the words in the box. Write the
words that name colors on the fish.
Write the other words on the boat.

Copyright © Houghton Mifflin Company. All rights reserved.

Word Bank

also
blue
brown
color
funny
green
like
many
some

Name _____

Words to Know

Write a word from the box to complete each sentence. Use the pictures to help you.

_____

1. The _____ has many animals.

_____

2. Some _____ like to eat krill.

_____

3. This _____ lives in the sea, too.

_____

4. We can _____ and get wet in the sea.

Name _____

What Did You See?

Read each question. Cut out and paste the correct answer under the question.

1. **Where's the funny fish?**

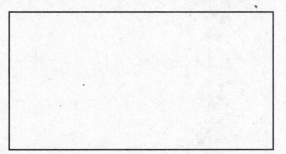

2. **What can grab?**

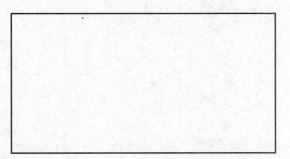

3. **What can zig and zag?**

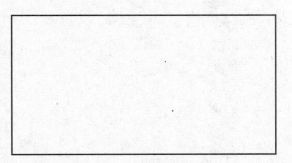

A crab can.

Here it is!

Some fish can zig and zag.

140

Name _____

Clusters with *r*

Write a word from the box to complete each sentence in the story.

Word Bank

| trip | crab | drip | grin | grab | trap |

1. Dan will go on a _____ .

2. He will _____ his bags.

3. Look at Dad _____ !

4. Dad and Dan set the _____ .

5. Dad has a big _____ .

6. Dan said, "Do not let it _____ on me!"

Theme 3: **Let's Look Around!**   141

Make Them Complete!

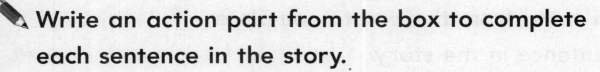

Write an action part from the box to complete
each sentence in the story.

gets a bass   jump   eat   fix the fish

_____

1. Some fish _____ .

2. Mom _____ .

3. Dad and the kids _____ .

4. Then they _____ !

Name _____

Spelling Spree

Add the missing letter to write each Spelling Word.

Spelling Words

trip
crab
drip
grin
grab
trap

1. t __ ap = _____

2. d __ ip = _____

3. g __ ab = _____

Proofread each sentence. Circle each Spelling Word that is wrong, and write it correctly.

4. We go on a tirp. _____

5. We get a krab! _____

6. We grinn. _____

Name _____

Writing Facts

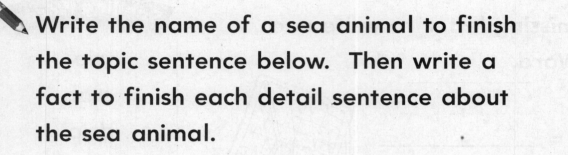 Write the name of a sea animal to finish
the topic sentence below. Then write a
fact to finish each detail sentence about
the sea animal.

Topic Sentence

_____
- -

1. Here are some facts about _____.

Detail Sentence

_____
- -

2. It has _____.

Detail Sentence

_____
- -

3. It can _____.

Detail Sentence

_____
- -

4. It eats _____.

144   Theme 3: **Let's Look Around!**

Name _____

Spelling Review

Each Spelling Word is missing one letter.
Write the missing letter.

Spelling Words

| drip | big | trap | an | grab | crab |

The missing letter is the first sound you hear

in  .   1. ___n

The missing letter is the first sound you hear

in  .   2. b___g

Write two letters to complete each Spelling
Word.

3. _____ab   4. _____ap

5. _____ab   6. _____ip

Name _____

Spelling Spree

✎ **Write a Spelling Word in each blank.**

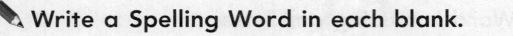

Spelling Words

| at | had | in | it | big | drip |

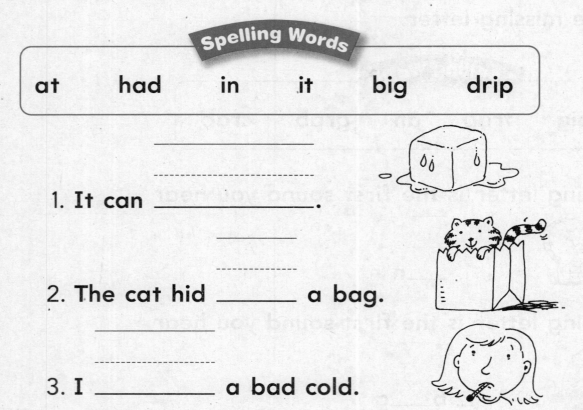

_____

- -

1. It can _____.

_____

- - - - - - - - - - - -

2. The cat hid _____ a bag.

_____

- - - - - - - - - - - - - - - -

3. I _____ a bad cold.

✎ **Proofread each sentence. Circle each Spelling
Word that is wrong, and write it correctly.**

_____

- - - - - - - - - - - - - - - - - - - -

4. I am on a bigg trip!

_____

- - - - - - - - - - - - - - - - - - - -

5. I look att a crab.

_____

- - - - - - - - - - - - - - - - - - - -

6. Et can grab.

Name _____

Clusters with /

Name each picture. Circle the letters that stand for the beginning sounds.

1. cr cl bl	2. sl gr gl	3. fr fl sl	4. pl pr cl
5. sl cl fl	6. gl fl sl	7. gl gr pl	8. pr sl pl
9. cl pl cr	10. bl pl gl	11. bl br sl	12. sl pl cl
13. fr fl sl	14. cl gl pl	15. cr sl bl	16. gl gr cl

Theme 4: **Family and Friends**   **147**

Name _____

Clusters with /

 Circle the word that names each picture.
Write the word.

1.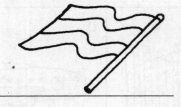
flat

flag

_____

2.
clock

class

_____

3.
glass

grass

_____

4.
block

blot

_____

5.
plug

slug

_____

6.
sled

slacks

_____

7.
flap

clap

_____

8.
flat

flip

_____

148   Theme 4: **Family and Friends**

Name _____

Words with Short *o*

Name each picture. Write **o** if the picture name has the short **o** sound.

1.	2.	3.	4.
5.	6.	7.	8.
9.	10.	11.	12.
13.	14.	15.	16.

Theme 4: **Family and Friends**   149

Name _____

Words with Short *o*

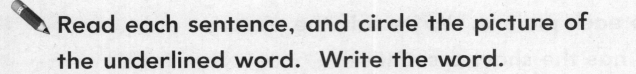 Read each sentence, and circle the picture of the underlined word. Write the word.

1. Dot can pack for a trip.

_____

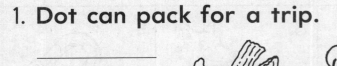 

2. Bob sees a clock.

_____

3. See Dot's doll.

_____

   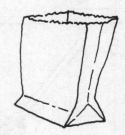

4. See Dot's socks.

_____

5. See Dot's blocks.

_____

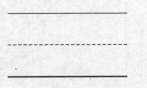 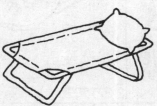  

150 Theme 4: **Family and Friends**

Name _____

Drawing Conclusions

Read the sentences. Write your conclusion.

1. **Dan is cold.**

   Dan sees a hat.

   _____

   -

   Dan will _____

   _____

   -

   _____

2. **The vet looks at the pet.**

   The pet is not sick.

   _____

   -

   The pet will _____

   _____

   -

   _____

Theme 4: **Family and Friends**   151

Name _____

Words to Know

Write a word from the box to complete
each sentence in the story.

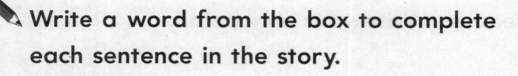

Word Bank

| your | love | picture | children |

Come see the people in my family.

_____

Here is a _____.

We have a mother, a father, and two

_____

_____.

We get lots of _____.

_____

Who's in _____ family?

Name _____

Words to Know

Cut out the pictures. Paste each picture
above the sentence that goes with it.

1.
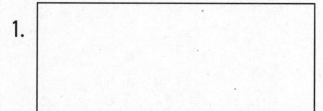

"Come here and see my
pictures," said Jan.

2.

Here is a picture of six
people.

3.

See the mother and
father hug the children.

4.

I love the picture of
your family.

Theme 4: **Family and Friends**   153

Name _____

Family Fun

Write a word from the box to complete each sentence.

Word Bank

| ball | garden | picnic | snap |

1. Some families like to pick food in a

   _____

   _____ .

2. Some families like to have

   _____

   ----

   a _____ .

3. Some families like to kick a _____ .

   _____

4. Some families also like to _____ pictures.

Name _____

Families

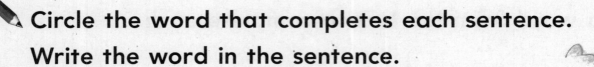

Circle the word that completes each sentence.
Write the word in the sentence.

_____
----

1. A family can have _____.

   and   children   go

_____
----

2. Families can get lots of _____.

   jump   love   four

_____
----

3. Some families have _____.

   pets   eat   fall

_____
----

4. Some families like to _____.

   cold   food   jog

Name _____

The Short *o* Sound

Write a word to complete each sentence.

| on | not | got | box | hot | top |

_____

1. It is _____.

_____

2. Tom _____ a big box.

_____

3. See what he did to the _____!

_____

4. The box is _____ Bob.

_____

5. It is on _____ of Bob.

_____

6. It's _____ hot in the box.

Theme 4: **Family and Friends**   157

Name _____

Make It a Sentence!

 Write a naming part to complete each sentence.

| The cat | Kim |

_____

1. _____ likes to kick and pass.

2. _____ likes to eat catnip.

 Write an action part to complete each sentence.

| lives in a den | gets a job |

_____

3. Dad _____.

4. The fox _____.

Name _____

Spelling Spree

Write the missing letter. Write the word.

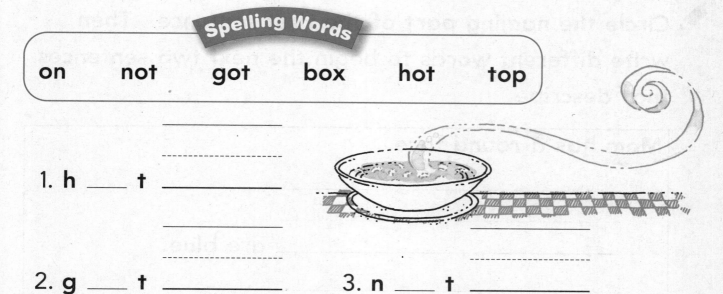

Spelling Words

| on | not | got | box | hot | top |

1. h __ t _____

2. g __ t _____   3. n __ t _____

Proofread each sentence. Circle each Spelling Word that is wrong, and write it correctly.

4. I have a big bocks. _____

5. Fran and I sit un it. _____

6. The tp falls in! _____

Beginning Sentences Different Ways

Circle the naming part of the first sentence. Then write different words to begin the next two sentences that describe.

Mom has a round face.

_____

1. _____ are blue.

_____

2. _____ wears red glasses.

Granddad smiles all the time.

_____

1. _____ has a loud laugh.

_____

2. _____ are strong.

Name _____

Clusters with *s*

Name each picture. Circle the letters that stand for the beginning sounds.

1. sc sl st	2. st sl sp	3. sp sm sl	4. st sm sp
5. sn sw sp	6. sl sw st	7. sl st sp	8. st sl sc
9. sc sn st	10. sk sp sw	11. sw st sl	12. sl sw sm
13. st sw sl	14. sn sl sp	15. st sk sl	16. sm sp sk

Theme 4: **Family and Friends**   **161**

Name _____

Clusters with *s*

Read each word. Write **s** before each word.
Read the new word.

1. ___**led**	2. ___**tick**	3. ___**nap**
4. ___**cat**	5. ___**pin**	6. ___**top**
7. ___**pot**	8. ___**kid**	9. ___**lip**
10. ___**mock**	11. ___**well**	12. ___**tack**

Name _____

Words with Short *e*

Name each picture. Write **e** if the picture
name has the short **e** sound.

1.	2.	3.	4.
5.	6.	7.	8.
9.	10.	11.	12.
13.	14.	15.	16.

Theme 4: **Family and Friends**   **163**

Name _____

Words with Short e

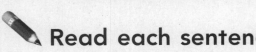 Read each sentence. Circle the picture of the underlined word. Write the word.

1. The bird has a <u>nest</u>.

_____
- - - - - - - - - - -
_____

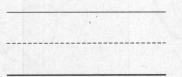 

2. The pig has a <u>pen</u>.

_____
- - - - - - - - - - -
_____

3. The bug has a <u>web</u>.

_____
- - - - - - - - - - -
_____

4. The cub has a <u>den</u>.

_____
- - - - - - - - - - -
_____

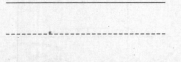 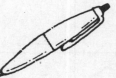  

5. Pat has a <u>bed</u>.

_____
- - - - - - - - - - -
_____

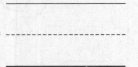 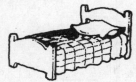 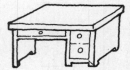

Name _____

Silent *kn, wr, gn*

Name each picture. Circle the pair of letters that begin each picture name. Write the two letters.

1.

   wr   kn

   _____

2.

   wr   kn

   _____

3.

   wr   kn

   _____

4.

   wr   kn

   _____

5.

   gn   wr

   _____

6.

   gn   wr

   _____

7.

   wr   gn

   _____

8.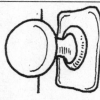

   kn   wr

   _____

9.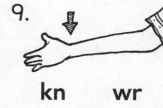

   kn   wr

   _____

Name _____

Alike and Different

Think about what a girl and a dog can do.
Read each phrase in the box. Write it in the
chart where it belongs.

| can not spell | can pick flowers | can eat |
| can jump | can not pick flowers | can spell |

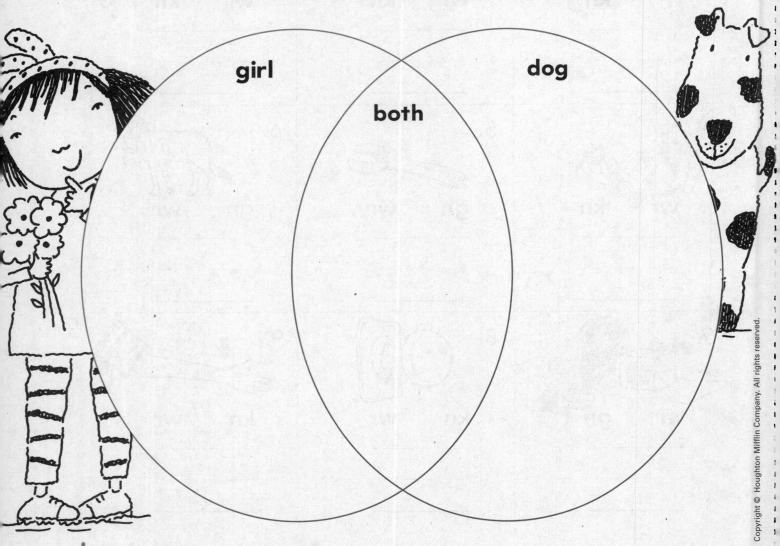

girl

dog

both

Name _____

Words to Know

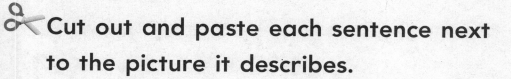

✂ Cut out and paste each sentence next to the picture it describes.

1.

2.

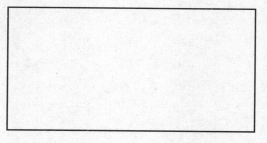

3.

I will write to Jan!

We can read, sing, and play.

Today I met a girl. I know she is my friend.

Name _____

Words to Know

Write words from the box to complete the story.

Word Bank

sing	read	today	play

Fran is my best friend.

_____

She can _____ like a bird.

_____

She can _____ tricks, too.

_____

I will write to Fran _____ .

I will tell my best friend what I did.

I know Fran will write back.

_____

I can _____ what she did, too!

Theme 4: **Family and Friends**   **169**

Name _____

The Big Day!

Read the story. Draw a picture to go with it.

One day there is a sign at the door.

First Prize for Best Picture

Jack got a picture of a boy and his dog.

Jack got first prize, and everyone smiled.

Name _____

The Best Pet Trick

Write a word from the box to complete each answer.

Word Bank

prize	Test	Peg

1. **What is on the sign?**

   All pets can come to the Best
   _____

   Pet _____.

2. **What trick did Slim do?**
   _____

   Slim and _____ did a
   "Knock, Knock" trick.

3. **Who did the best pet trick?**
   _____

   Slim did! Slim got the _____.

Theme 4: **Family and Friends**   **171**

Name _____

The Short *e* Sound

✏️ Say each picture name. Write the word from the box that begins with the same sound.

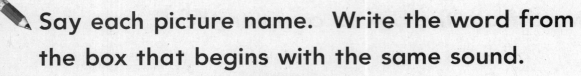
Spelling Words

get   ten   red   pet   men   yes

1. _____

_____

2. _____

_____

3. _____

_____

4. _____

_____

5. _____

_____

6. _____

_____

172   Theme 4: **Family and Friends**

Name _____

Find the Sentence

Read each group of words. Underline each telling sentence.

Mom calls to me.

Mom

Bob sings.
sings

Dad looks at the paper.

looks at the paper

wins the prize

Bob wins the prize.

Name _____

Spelling Spree

Write the Spelling Words that rhyme with **pen** under the 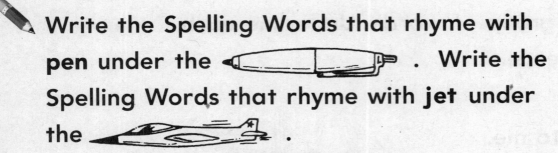 . Write the Spelling Words that rhyme with **jet** under the .

Spelling Words

| get | ten | red | pet | men | yes |

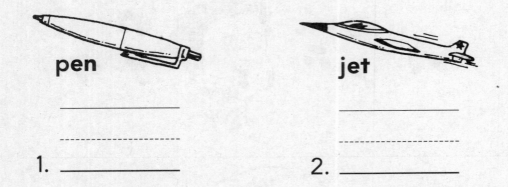

pen

jet

1. _____   2. _____

3. _____   4. _____

Proofread each sentence. Circle each Spelling Word that is wrong, and write it correctly.

5. I like the color redd. _____

6. Yez, I do. _____

Showing Strong Feelings

Finish these sentences that tell your opinion about
Lucy learning Oscar's secret code. Write one
exclamation that shows a strong feeling.

Topic Sentence

1. I think Lucy _____ .

Detail Sentence

2. One reason is _____ .

Detail Sentence

3. Another reason is _____ .

Name _____

Triple Clusters

Read the story. Write each word in dark print next to the picture it names.

Big Gus **splits** the logs.
The **scraps** go in the bin.
Big Gus **scrubs** up.
He **strums** and hums.

1.  _____

2. _____

3.  _____

4.  _____

Name _____

Words with Short *u*

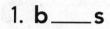

Write **u** to complete each word. Then write
two of the words to complete the sentence.

1. b___s

2. dr___m

3. f___n

4. t___b

5. d___ck

6. j___st

7. The _____ swims in the _____ .

Name _____

Words with Short *u*

Read each word in dark print. Circle and
write the rhyming word in the box.

bug	tug	**fun**	but
_____	sun	_____	luck
_____	cub	_____	run
nut	hum	**buzz**	slug
_____	cut	_____	rug
_____	duck	_____	fuzz
gum	club	**dust**	must
_____	plum	_____	hug
_____	puff	_____	jump

Name _____

Put Them in Order!

Think about **The Best Pet.** Cut out the pictures and sentences, and paste them in order.

1

2

3

Slim gets first prize!

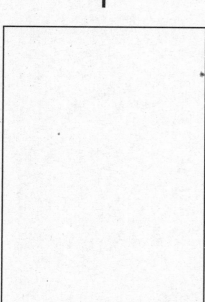

The girls see a sign.

Slim does a fun trick.

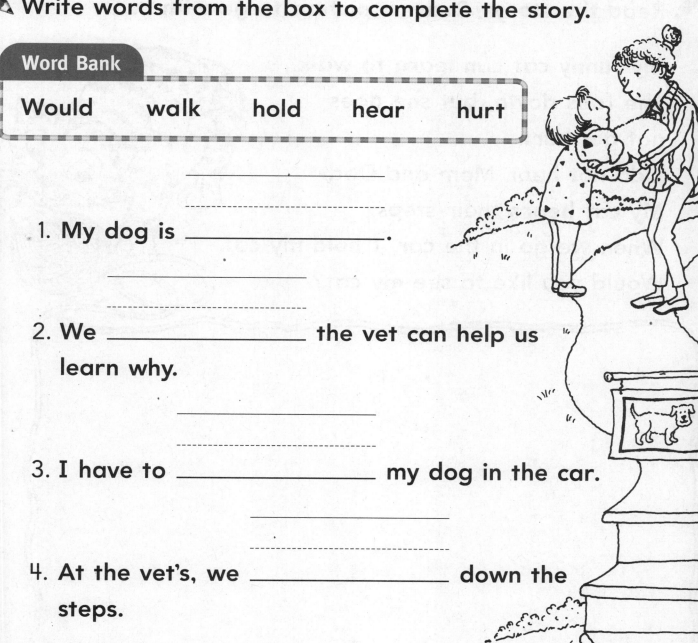

Name _____

Words to Know

Write words from the box to complete the story.

Word Bank

| Would | walk | hold | hear | hurt |

1. My dog is _____.

2. We _____ the vet can help us learn why.

3. I have to _____ my dog in the car.

4. At the vet's, we _____ down the steps.

5. _____ the vet help my dog?

Name _____

Words to Know

✏️ **Read the story. Draw a picture to go with it.**

My funny cat can learn to walk.
She falls down, but she does
not get hurt.
I do not hear Mom and Dad.
My cat hears their steps.
When we go in the car, I hold my cat.
Would you like to see my cat?

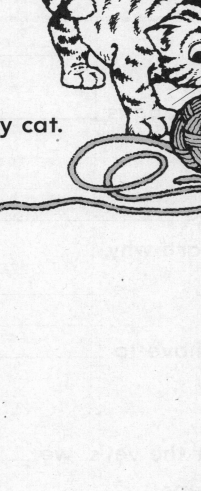

At the Pet Shop

Circle the word that completes each sentence.
Write the word.

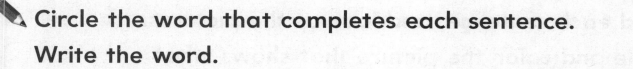

1. Judd felt glad his big _____ had come!

   day   down

2. He and Dad walked to the pet _____ .

   step   shop

3. "The _____ are we get one pup," said Dad.

   read   rules

4. "I hear a _____," said Judd. "What a pup!"

   noise   nose

Name _____

What's Happening?

Read each sentence, and look at the pictures.
Circle and color the picture that shows what
happens in **Bud's Day Out.**

1. Bud is Ben's pet.

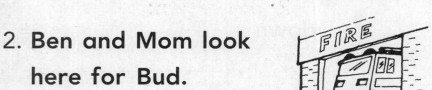

2. Ben and Mom look here for Bud.

3. Ben and Mom find Bud here.

Write what happens at the end of the story.

_____
_____
_____
_____

Name _____

The Short *u* Sound

Read each clue. Write **the correct** Spelling
Word from the box.

Spelling Words

| up | us | but | fun | cut | run |

1. not walk:

_____

- - - - - - - - - - - -

_____

2. not down:

_____

- - - - - - - - - - - -

_____

3. like we:

_____

- - - - - - - - - - - -

_____

4. what tricks are:

_____

- - - - - - - - - - - -

_____

Write the two words that rhyme with hut.

5. _____

- - - - - - - - - - - -

_____

6. _____

- - - - - - - - - - - -

_____

Theme 4: **Family and Friends**   185

Where's the Question?

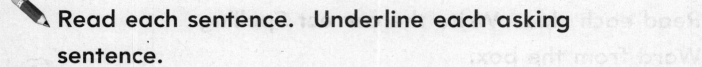 Read each sentence. Underline each asking sentence.

1. The class play is today.

   What day is it?

   _____

2. Who is in the play?

   The play has animals.

   _____

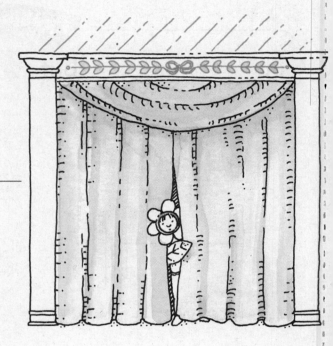

3. Can we go to the play?

   I can write a play.

   _____

4. The play is fun.

   Where is the next play?

Name _____

Spelling Spree

Use the letter shapes to make Spelling Words.

Spelling Words

| up | us | but | fun | cut | run |

1. _____
_____

2. _____
_____

3. _____
_____

Proofread each sentence. Circle each Spelling Word that is wrong, and write it correctly.

4. I like to runn. _____

5. It is a lot of fon. _____

6. I can run ub a hill. _____

Theme 4: **Family and Friends**   **187**

Exact Action Words

Draw a picture of an animal for a story. Give your animal a name.

Name: _____

Finish these story sentences about your animal. Use exact action words.

1. _____ is a _____.
   name   kind of animal

2. One day _____ _____ in a hole.
   name   exact action word

3. Then _____ _____.
   name   exact action word

4. _____ wants to _____!
   name   exact action word

Name _____

Spelling Review

Write a Spelling Word next to each number.

Spelling Words

| on | yes | box | ten | but | fun |

1. _____

2. _____

3. _____

4. _____

5. _____

6. _____

Which words have the short *e* sound?
Color those birds red.
Which words have the short *u* sound?
Color those birds blue.
Which words have the short *o* sound?
Color those birds brown.

Name _____

Spelling Spree

 Write the Spelling Word for each clue.

Spelling Words

| hot | get | run | yes | up | fun |

_____

1. not cold   _____

2. not no   _____

3. not down   _____

 Proofread each sentence. Circle each Spelling
Word that is wrong, and write it correctly.

_____

4. We had fon today.   _____

5. She loves to runn and play.   _____

6. Come git your pup today!   _____

My Handbook

192

Contents

Andy Apple

Benny Bear

Callie Cat

Dudley Duck

Edna Elephant

Fifi Fish

Gertie Goose

Hattie Horse

Iggy Iguana

Jumping Jill

Keely Kangaroo

Larry Lion

Mimi Mouse

Nyle Noodle

Ozzie Octopus

Pippa Pig

Queenie Queen

Reggie Rooster

Sammy Seal

Tiggy Tiger

Umbie Umbrella

Vinny Volcano

Willy Worm

Mr. X-Ray

Yetta Yo-Yo

Zelda Zebra

1. Look at the letters from left to right.

2. Think about the sounds for the letters, and look for word parts you know.

3. Blend the sounds to read the word.

4. Ask yourself: Is it a word I know? Does it make sense in what I am reading?

5. If not, ask yourself: What else can I try?

Predict/Infer

► Think about the title, the illustrations, and what you have read so far.

► Tell what you think will happen next or what you will learn.

Question

► Ask yourself questions as you read.

Monitor/Clarify

► Ask yourself if what you are reading makes sense.

► If you don't understand something, reread, read ahead, or use the illustrations.

Summarize

► Think about the main ideas or the important parts of the story.

► Tell the important things in your own words.

Evaluate

► Ask yourself: Do I like what I have read? Am I learning what I wanted to know?

Writing the Alphabet

Trace and write the letters.

Aa Aa

Bb Bb

Cc Cc

Dd Dd

Ee Ee

Ff Ff

Gg Gg

Trace and write the letters.

Hh Hh

Ii Ii

Jj Jj

Kk Kk

Ll Ll

Mm Mm

Trace and write the letters.

Nn Nn

Oo Oo

Pp Pp

Qq Qq

Rr Rr

Ss Ss

Tt Tt

Trace and write the letters.

Uu Uu

Vv Vv

Ww Ww

Xx Xx

Yy Yy

Zz Zz

Trace and write the letters.

A a   A a

B b   B b

C c   C c

D d   D d

E e   E e

F f   F f

G g   G g

Trace and write the letters.

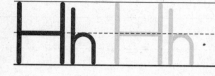

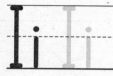

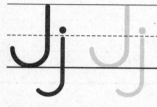

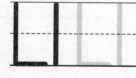

Trace and write the letters.

N n   N n

O o   O o

P p   P p

Q q   Q q

R r   R r

S s   S s

T t   T t

Trace and write the letters.

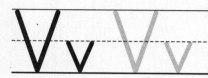

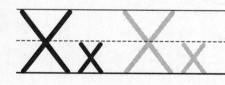

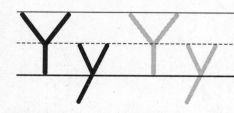

How to Study a Word

1. **LOOK** at the word.

2. **SAY** the word.

3. **THINK** about the word.

4. **WRITE** the word.

5. **CHECK** the spelling.

A

a
about
again
always
and
any
around
as

B

back
because
before

C

cannot
come
coming
could

D

do
down

F

for
friend
from

G

getting
goes
going

H

has
have
her
here
his
house
how

I

I
if
into
is

L

little

M

many
more

N

never
new
now

O

of

one

or

other

our

out

over

P

people

R

right

S

said

some

T

than

the

their

there

they

thing

to

tried

two

V

very

W

want

was

were

what

when

where

who

would

Y

you

your

Mr. C's Dinner

The Short *i* sound

in

it

him

Spelling Words

1. in
2. it
3. him
4. big
5. sit
6. did

Challenge Words

1. dish
2. milk

My Study List
Add your own
spelling words
on the back. ➡

Seasons

The Short *a* sound

an

at

can

Spelling Words

1. an
2. at
3. can
4. cat
5. had
6. man

Challenge Words

1. catch
2. add

My Study List
Add your own
spelling words
on the back. ➡

Name _____

 My Study List

_____

_____

1. _____

_____

2. _____

_____

3. _____

_____

4. _____

_____

5. _____

_____

6. _____

Name _____

 My Study List

_____

_____

1. _____

_____

2. _____

_____

3. _____

_____

4. _____

_____

5. _____

_____

6. _____

Let's Look Around!
Spelling Review

Spelling Words

1. an
2. in
3. trap
4. at
5. it
6. crab
7. had
8. big
9. drip
10. grab

See the back for Challenge Words.

My Study List
Add your own spelling words on the back. ➡

What a Trip!

Consonant Clusters with *r*	
trip	crab
drip	grin

Spelling Words

1. trip
2. crab
3. drip
4. grin
5. grab
6. trap

Challenge Words

1. crack
2. brown

My Study List
Add your own spelling words on the back. ➡

Name _____

📝 My Study List

_____

1. _____

2. _____

3. _____

4. _____

5. _____

6. _____

Name _____

📝 My Study List

_____

1. _____

2. _____

3. _____

4. _____

5. _____

6. _____

Challenge Words

1. add
2. dish
3. crack

The Best Pet

The Short *e* sound

get

ten

red

Spelling Words

1. get
2. ten
3. red
4. pet
5. men
6. yes

Challenge Words

1. tent
2. bell

My Study List
Add your own
spelling words
on the back. ➡

Who's in a Family?

The Short *o* sound

on

not

box

Spelling Words

1. on
2. not
3. got
4. box
5. hot
6. top

Challenge Words

1. pond
2. doll

My Study List
Add your own
spelling words
on the back. ➡

Name _____

 My Study List

_____

1. _____

2. _____

3. _____

4. _____

5. _____

6. _____

Name _____

 My Study List

_____

1. _____

2. _____

3. _____

4. _____

5. _____

6. _____

Family and Friends
Spelling Review

Spelling Words

1. on
2. get
3. up
4. hot
5. ten
6. but
7. box
8. fun
9. yes
10. run

See the back for Challenge Words.

My Study List
Add your own spelling words on the back. ➡

215

Bud's Day Out

The Short *u* sound

up

us

but

Spelling Words

1. up
2. us
3. but
4. fun
5. cut
6. run

Challenge Words

1. jump
2. plum

My Study List
Add your own spelling words on the back. ➡

215

Name _____

 My Study List

_____

1. _____

_____

2. _____

_____

3. _____

_____

4. _____

_____

5. _____

_____

6. _____

Name _____

My Study List

_____

1. _____

_____

2. _____

_____

3. _____

_____

4. _____

_____

5. _____

_____

6. _____

Challenge Words

1. pond
2. bell
3. plum

Proofreading Marks

Answer these questions when you check your writing.

☐ Did I begin each sentence with a capital letter?

☐ Did I use the right mark at the end of each sentence? (. ?)

☐ Did I spell each word correctly?

Proofreading Marks		
∧	Add	My aunt came to visit.
—	Take out	We ~~were~~ sang songs.
/	Make a capital letter a small letter.	The Ðogs hid from the storm.
⹀	Make a small letter a capital letter.	There are thirty days in april.

Name _____

My Friends

Draw pictures of your friends doing things they like. Write labels that tell about your pictures.

Draw four friends. Show details that tell who and what. Write two labels for each picture.

My Friends	

Name _____

At School

Draw pictures of you and your friends doing things they like. Write labels that tell about your pictures.

Draw four school activities. Show details that tell who, what, and where. Write two labels for each picture.

At School	

Name _____

Planning My Sentences

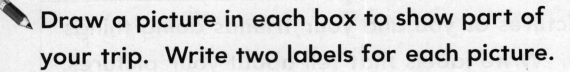 Draw a picture in each box to show part of your trip. Write two labels for each picture.

Name _____

Planning My Sentences

Draw a picture in each box to show something
that happened in your town. Write two labels
for each picture.

Name _____

Planning Sentences
That Tell a Story

 Write the sentences in order.

_____

_____

Title: _____

First

↓

Next

↓

Last

Name _____

Planning Sentences That Tell a Story

✏️ **Write the sentences in order.**

_____

- - - - - - - - - - - - - - - - - -

Topic: _____

First

↓

Next

↓

Last

Planning My Sentences

Write and draw details that describe your favorite season. You do not have to write words for every sense.

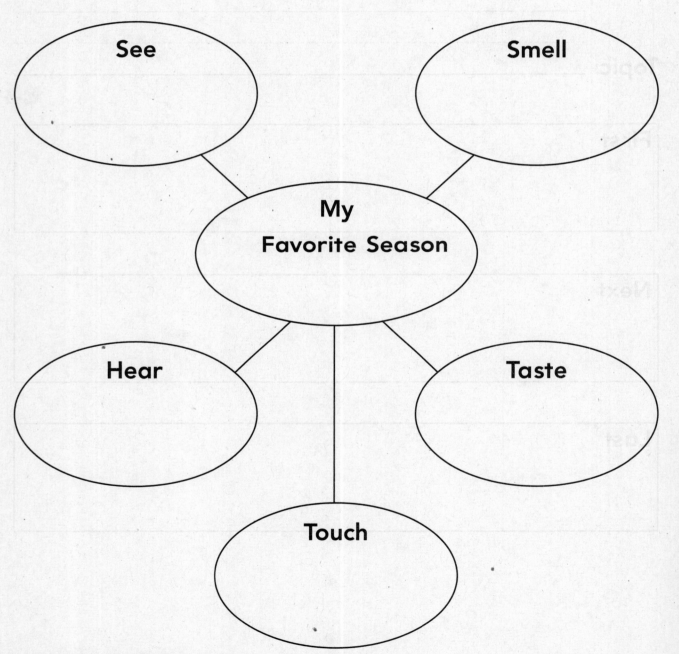

Name _____

Writing Traits Rubric

Read your paper. Check the boxes that tell about your sentences.

My Sentences

Superstar

☐ I used words that tell how my topic looks, sounds, smells, tastes, and feels.

☐ All of my sentences are about one topic.

☐ I wrote complete sentences.

Rising Star

☐ I need to add more words that tell how my topic looks, sounds, smells, tastes, and feels.

☐ Not all of my sentences are about the same topic.

☐ Some of my sentences are not complete.

Name _____

Planning My Instructions

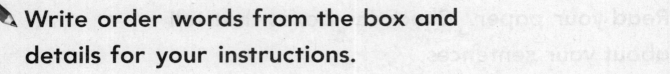 Write order words from the box and details for your instructions.

My Topic: How to make _____

Word Bank

First	Next	Then	Last

1. Order Word	Step
_____	

2. Order Word	Step
_____	

3. Order Word	Step
_____	

4. Order Word	Step
_____	

226   Theme 3: **Let's Look Around!**

Name _____

Writing Traits Rubric

Read your paper. Check the boxes that tell about your sentences.

My Sentences

Superstar

- ☐ My instructions have order words.
- ☐ I told what to do in order.
- ☐ I wrote complete sentences.

Rising Star

- ☐ I need to add order words to some of my detail sentences.
- ☐ My steps need to be put in the correct order.
- ☐ Some of my sentences are not complete.

Name _____

Planning My Sentences

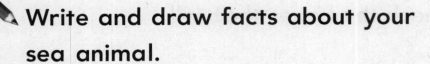 Write and draw facts about your
sea animal.

My Topic

Fact 1

Fact 2

Name _____

Writing Traits Rubric

Read your paper. Check the boxes that tell about your sentences.

My Sentences

Superstar

- [ ] My topic sentence tells what my detail sentences are about.
- [ ] My detail sentences tell facts.
- [ ] I began every sentence with a capital letter.

Rising Star

- [ ] I need a topic sentence that tells what my detail sentences are about.
- [ ] Some of my detail sentences need facts.
- [ ] Some of my sentences do not begin with a capital letter.

Theme 3: **Let's Look Around!**   **229**

Name _____

Planning My Sentences

Write sentences that describe someone in your family.

Write and draw details that describe your topic.
You do not have to write words for every sense.

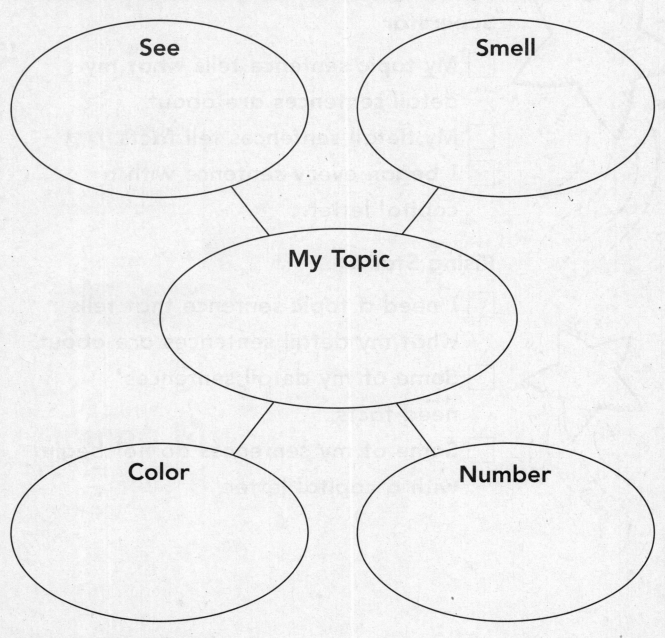

Writing Traits Rubric

Read your paper. Check the boxes that tell about your sentences.

My Sentences

Superstar

☐ All of my sentences are about one topic.

☐ My sentences begin with different words.

☐ I used many sense words to describe my topic.

Rising Star

☐ Not all of my sentences are about the same topic.

☐ Most of my sentences start with the same word.

☐ I need to add sense words to describe my topic.

Week 2

Writing Writing Response to Literature

Planning My Sentences

 Write a topic sentence to tell your opinion.
Then write reasons that tell why.

Topic Sentence

First Reason

Second Reason

Name _____

Writing Traits Rubric

Read your paper. Check the boxes that tell about your sentences.

My Sentences

Superstar

☐ I used exclamations to show my strong feelings.

☐ I included a topic sentence.

☐ I wrote reasons that explain my opinion.

Rising Star

☐ I need to add exclamations to show my strong feelings.

☐ I need to add a topic sentence.

☐ I need to give reasons that explain my opinion.

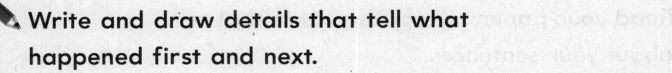

Name _____

Planning My Sentences

Write and draw details that tell what
happened first and next.

My Topic: _____

First

↓

Second

Name _____

Writing Traits Rubric

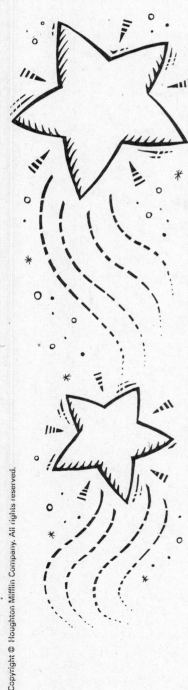

Read your paper. Check the boxes that tell
about your sentences.

My Sentences

Superstar

☐ My sentences have exact action
words.

☐ My sentences have interesting details.

☐ Every sentence has a naming part
and an action part.

Rising Star

☐ I need to use more exact action
words.

☐ I need to add interesting details to
my sentences.

☐ Not all of my sentences have a
naming part and an action part.

A	A	A	B	B	C	C	D	D
E	E	E	F	F	G	G	H	H
I	I	J	J	K	K	L	L	M
M	N	N	O	O	P	P	Q	Q
R	R	S	S	T	T	U	U	V
V	W	W	X	X	Y	Y	Z	Z

You can add punctuation marks or other letters to the blanks.

Letter Tray

↓

Letter Tray

fold

fold

fold

d	d	c	c	b	b	a	a	a
h	h	g	g	f	f	e	e	e
m	l	l	k	k	j	j	i	i
q	q	p	p	o	o	n	n	m
v	u	u	t	t	s	s	r	r
z	z	y	y	x	x	w	w	v

Aa

Bb

Cc

Dd

Ee

Ff

Gg

Hh

Ii

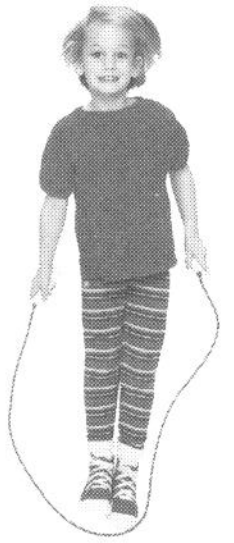

Jj

Kk

Ll

Mm

Nn

Oo

Pp

Qq

Rr

Ss

Tt

Uu

Vv

Ww

Xx

 a

 i

 qu_

 b

j
ge
gi_
_dge

 r
wr_

 c
k
ck
_ck

 k
c
_ck

 s
ce
ci_

 d
_ed

 l
_le

 t
_ed
_

 e

 m

 u

 f

 n
kn_
gn

 v

 g

 o

 w

 h

 p

 _x

or	o	Yy
ir	u	Zz
ar	e	sh
	oo	th
	oo	wh
	ow	ch
	oy	a
	aw	i

 y_

 o o_e oa ow _oe

 or ore

 z _s

 u u_e _ue ew

 ir er ur

 sh

 e e_e ee ea _y ie_

 ar

 th

 oo

 wh

 oo ew ue ou u u_e

 ch _tch

 ow ou

 a a_e ai _ay

 _oy oi

 i i_e ie igh _y

 aw au

Theme 1, Week 3	Theme 1, Week 2	Theme 1, Week 1
a	and	go
find	here	on
have	jump	the
one	not	
to	too	
who	we	

Theme 1, Week 3	Theme 1, Week 2	Theme 1, Week 1

You can add your own words for sentence building.

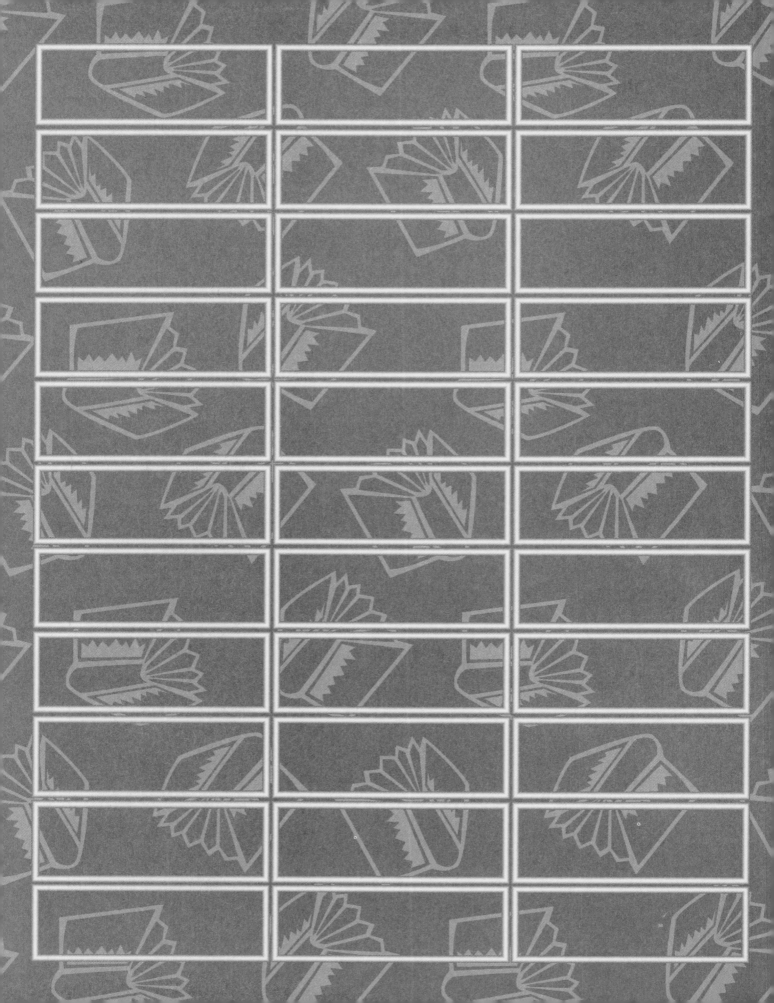

Theme 2, Week 3	Theme 2, Week 2	Theme 2, Week 1
are	do	five
away	for	four
does	is	in
he	me	once
live	my	three
pull	said	two
they	you	upon
where	I	what

Theme 2, Week 3	Theme 2, Week 2	Theme 2, Week 1

You can add your own words for sentence building.

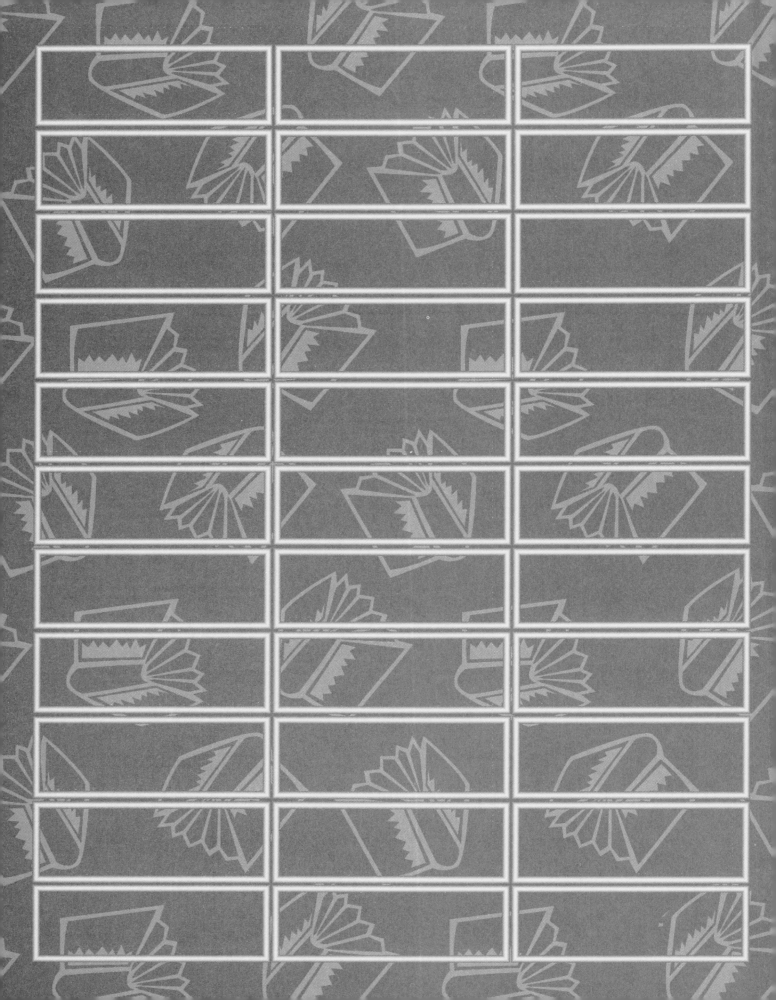

Theme 3, Week 3	Theme 3, Week 2	Theme 3, Week 1
also	all	animal
blue	call	bird
brown	eat	cold
color	every	fall
funny	first	flower
green	never	full
like	paper	look
many	shall	of
some	why	see

You can add your own words for sentence building.

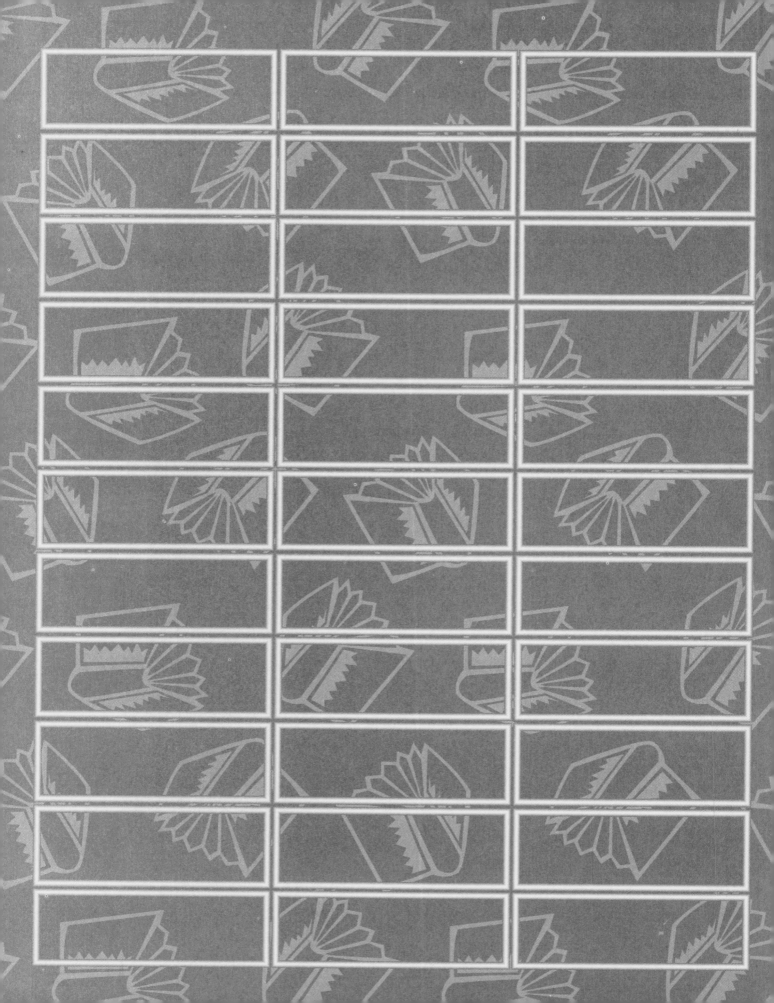

Theme 4, Week 3	Theme 4, Week 2	Theme 4, Week 1
car	play	come
down	friend	children
walk	girl	family
hear	she	father
hold	read	love
hurt	sing	mother
learn	today	people
their	write	picture
would	know	your

You can add your own words for sentence building.

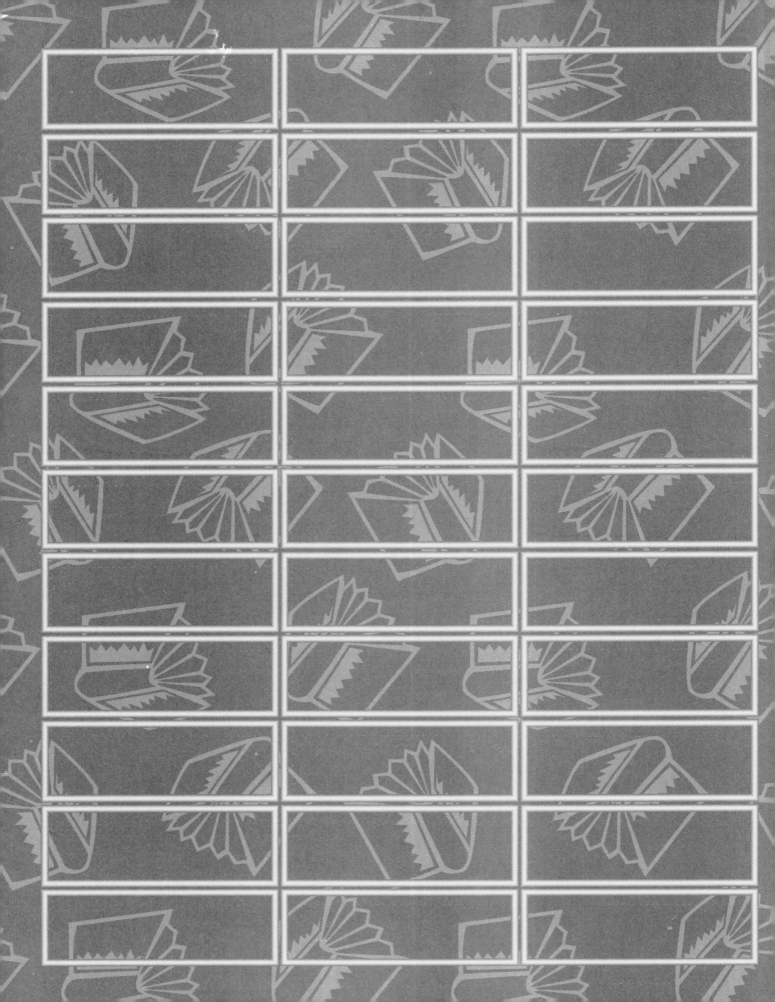